D0925177

Trail Guide to Geology
of the Upper Pecos

FOR THOSE WHO
venture on high trails with eyes to see,
and leave nature as it was meant to be.

Scenic Trips to the Geologic Past
No. 6, *revised*

New Mexico Bureau of Mines & Mineral Resources

A DIVISION OF
NEW MEXICO INSTITUTE OF MINING & TECHNOLOGY

Trail Guide to Geology of the Upper Pecos

by PATRICK K. SUTHERLAND
AND ARTHUR MONTGOMERY

*Illustrated by David H. Moneypenny
and Neila M. Pearson*

Frontispiece:

PECOS BALDY LAKE AND VIEW
NORTH TO TRUCHAS PEAKS
Trace of major fault with
Precambrian quartzite to left,
and Pennsylvanian sedimentary
rocks to right.

SOCORRO 1975

NEW MEXICO INSTITUTE OF MINING & TECHNOLOGY
KENNETH W. FORD, *President*

NEW MEXICO BUREAU OF MINES & MINERAL RESOURCES
FRANK E. KOTTLOWSKI, *Director*
GEORGE S. AUSTIN, *Deputy Director*

BOARD OF REGENTS

Ex Officio
Bruce King, *Governor of New Mexico*
Leonard DeLayo, *Superintendent of Public Instruction*

Appointed
William G. Abbott, President, 1961-1985, *Hobbs*
Judy Floyd, 1977-1987, *Las Cruces*
Owen Lopez, 1977-1983, *Santa Fe*
Dave Rice, 1972-1983, *Carlsbad*
Steve Torres, Secretary-Treasurer, 1967-1985, *Socorro*

BUREAU STAFF

Full Time

MARLA D. ADKINS, *Assistant Editor*
ORIN J. ANDERSON, *Geologist*
RUBEN ARCHULETA, *Technician I*
KEVIN C. BAKER, *Field Researcher*
ROBERT A. BIEBERMAN, *Senior Petrol. Geologist*
STEVE BLODGETT, *Assistant Editor*
LYNN A. BRANDVOLD, *Chemist*
JAMES C. BRANNAN, *Draftsperson*
CORALE BRIERLEY, *Chemical Microbiologist*
BRENDA R. BROADWELL, *Assoc. Lab Geoscientist*
FRANK CAMPBELL, *Coal Geologist*
RICHARD CHAMBERLIN, *Economic Geologist*
CHARLES E. CHAPIN, *Senior Geologist*
JEANETTE CHAVEZ, *Admin. Secretary I*
RICHARD R. CHAVEZ, *Assistant Head, Petroleum*
RUBEN A. CRESPIN, *Laboratory Technician II*
LOIS M. DEVLIN, *Director, Bus.-Pub. Office*
KATHY C. EDEN, *Editorial Technician*
ROBERT W. EVELETH, *Mining Engineer*
K. BABETTE FARIS, *X-ray Lab. Manager*
ROUSSEAU H. FLOWER, *Sr. Emeritus Paleontologist*
STEPHEN J. FROST, *Coal Geologist*
JOHN W. HAWLEY, *Environmental Geologist*
DANA M. HELJESON, *Editorial Technician*
STEPHEN C. HOOK, *Paleontologist*
MELVIN JENNINGS, *Metallurgist*
BARBARA J. JOHNSON, *Staff Secretary*
ROBERT W. KELLEY, *Editor & Geologist*
SHERRY A. KRUKOWSKI, *Record Manager*
MARK LOGSDON, *Economic Geologist*
ANNABELLE LOPEZ, *Clerk Typist*

DAVID W. LOVE, *Environmental Geologist*
WESS MAULDIN, *Driller's Helper*
VIRGINIA MCLEMORE, *Geologist*
LYNNE MCNEIL, *Staff Secretary*
NORMA J. MEEKS, *Department Secretary*
DAVID MENZIE, *Geologist*
ARLEEN MONTOYA, *Librarian/Typist*
TERESA A. MUELLER, *Draftsperson*
SUE NESS, *Receptionist*
ROBERT M. NORTH, *Mineralogist*
KEITH O'BRIEN, *Hydrologist*
JOANNE C. OSBURN, *Coal Geologist*
GLENN R. OSBURN, *Volcanologist*
JOAN C. PENDLETON, *Associate Editor*
BARBARA R. POPP, *Lab. Biotechnologist*
ROBERT QUICK, *Driller*
MARSHALL A. REITER, *Senior Geophysicist*
JACQUES R. RENAULT, *Senior Geologist*
JAMES M. ROBERTSON, *Mining Geologist*
GRETCHEN H. ROYBAL, *Coal Geologist*
AMY SHACKLETT, *Asst. Lab Biotechnologist*
JACKIE H. SMITH, *Laboratory Technician IV*
DALE STALEY, *Driller's Helper*
WILLIAM J. STONE, *Hydrogeologist*
SAMUEL THOMPSON III, *Petroleum Geologist*
JUDY M. VAIZA, *Executive Secretary*
DEBRA VETTERMAN, *Draftsperson*
ROBERT H. WEBER, *Senior Geologist*
DONALD WOLBERG, *Vertebrate Paleontologist*
MICHAEL W. WOOLDRIDGE, *Scientific Illustrator*

Part Time

CHRISTINA L. BALK, *Geologist*
HOWARD B. NICKELSON, *Coal Geologist*

BEVERLY OHLINE, *Newswriter, Information Services*
THOMAS E. ZIMMERMAN, *Chief Security Officer*

Graduate Students

BRUCE W. BAKER
INDIRA BALKISSOON
GERRY W. CLARKSON

ROBERTA EGGLESTON
TED EGGLESTON
ADRIAN HUNT

TOM MCANULTY
LAWRENCE NELSON
JOHN YOUNG

Plus about 50 undergraduate assistants

First edition, 1960
Second edition, 1967
Reprinted 1968, 1971, 1972
Third edition, revised, 1975
Third edition, reprinted, 1981

Published by Authority of State of New Mexico, NMSA 1953 Sec. 63-1-4
Printed by University of New Mexico Printing Plant, May, 1981

Available from New Mexico Bureau of Mines & Mineral Resources, Socorro, NM 87801 $4.00

Preface

to this completely revised 3rd edition

The area featured in this guide encompasses the headwaters of the Pecos River and the broad 20-mile long valley opening northward from the town of Pecos. Most of the area is true wilderness; the main divides on the west and north have numerous spectacular peaks and ridges rising well above timberline—the highest peak towering over 13,000 ft. The intervening upper Pecos drainage basin is characterized by rugged, deep canyons separated by broad, gently sloping ridges and mesas covered by a pleasing mixture of dense spruce forests, majestic aspen stands, and open grassy meadows commonly filled with wild flowers in the summer months.

Thousands of persons visit the upper Pecos region each year, attracted by its incomparable beauty, recreational and guest ranch facilities, and good fishing. We hope this guidebook will encourage some to spend more time walking or riding the high trails, looking at the sharp peaks and mighty canyons with fresh insight, and provide new understanding of the geologic forces that have sculptured these awesome features.

Although the trail guide may be read solely for background information on the geology of the southern Sangre de Cristo Mountains, it can be best utilized while riding or hiking over the high mountain trails. Before setting out on a trail trip, read the entire description for that trip. You will then be watching for certain geologic features along the way. While it is one thing to appreciate an alpine peak, a waterfall, or a deep canyon for its scenic beauty, it is another to attempt to unravel the particular history of each feature—for the rocks that underlie the peaks, canyons and waterfalls provide the clues to a better understanding of earth history.

All trails were retraversed during the summer of 1974. Some present-day signs may fall into decay or be destroyed. Later improvements and changes in trails obviously will not appear in the text descriptions. If ever in doubt as to your location, give priority to your own identification of such major features as streams and mountains.

Distances and time schedules for all trips are approximate. Remember distances walked or ridden are always somewhat greater than those listed; hikers, riders, and trails simply do not go in straight lines in wild terrain. Also, the effort and time spent in climbing at high altitude always proves greater than anticipated. Time schedules, therefore, are only suggestions of what active people and horses can accomplish at a normal pace. Fast walkers will better the times given; slow walkers should allow an extra hour or two for most trips.

Wear comfortable clothes: choose your shoes (or boots) and socks with care. Blisters or sore feet can spoil a trip. For longer trips, especially, boots should be well broken-in; socks should not be old and thin.

The geology and trail map (in pocket) will hopefully arouse your curiosity and interest. We urge you to read the section in the text explaining the use and interpretation of this map. Above all, the accuracy of trails will prove of practical benefit to visitors in the upper Pecos high country, regardless of their degree of interest in the geology of the area. Much care has been devoted to locating the trails on the map; in fact, it presents the clearest, most accurate picture of the main trails of the region yet compiled. To fully utilize both the trail guide and geologic map, a magnetic compass is essential: not only for orienting yourself on trails, but for sharing the authors' interpretation of scenic and geologic features.

continued

Some geologic terms are explained in the text. Others are defined in the glossary at the rear.

We are indebted to many people for assistance and courtesies. During the preparation of the 1st edition (summer of 1959), we received the kindest hospitality and helpful information on the history of the region from the late Katherine Chavez Kavanagh, of Los Pinos guest ranch, after whom Lake Katherine is named. During fieldwork in the summer of 1974 for revisions of the 3rd edition, the present owners of Los Pinos ranch, Bill and Alice McSweeney, were extremely helpful and hospitable. David J. Kitts provided outstanding field assistance during the revision of the guide in the summer of 1974. Elliott Barker, author of *Beatty's Cabin,* and the most knowledgable living person concerning the early history of the upper Pecos, provided interesting and useful information about the region and trails. James H. Russell kindly supplied a historical account of the Pecos mine. During our restudy of all trails in the summer of 1974, Charles Wright and George Edwards, rangers for the Pecos Ranger District of the Santa Fe National Forest, provided extensive help and assisted us in traversing the incomparable Sky Line trail added to the 3rd edition.

The original cover sketch drawn for the 1960 edition by David H. Moneypenny was redesigned by illustrator Neila M. Pearson to conform to the Bureau's revised styling of covers.

Patrick K. Sutherland
Professor of Geology
University of Oklahoma

Norman, Oklahoma and
Easton, Pennsylvania
February, 1975

Arthur Montgomery
Professor Emeritus of Geology
Lafayette College

Contents

FIGURES

PHOTOGRAPHS

COLOR PLATES

(following page 24)

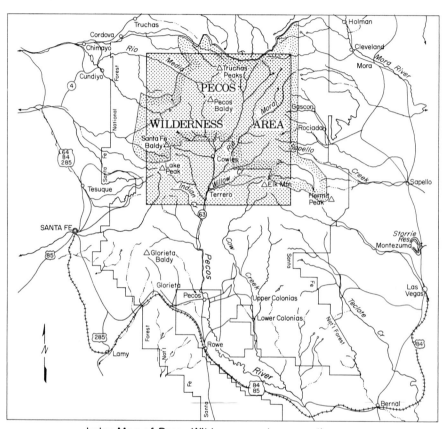

Index Map of Pecos Wilderness and surrounding area

④   State highways   Pecos Wilderness boundary

⑧⑤   U.S. highways   Area covered by Trail Guide

Introduction

The mountainous area described in this booklet is in the southern Sangre de Cristo Range, which lies at the southernmost end of the thousand-mile-long Rocky Mountain system. This area of breathtaking scenery and exceptional geologic interest encompasses one of the most beautiful recreational and wilderness regions in the Southwest, with game, trout streams, conifer and aspen forests, alpine flowers, and towering 13,000-ft peaks.

The upper Pecos high country is named for the Pecos River, one of the great rivers of New Mexico, which heads in this region. The little town of Pecos, the gateway to the area, lies about midway between Santa Fe and Las Vegas on a branch alternate of US-84-85. NM-63 runs northward from Pecos for 20 miles along the deep Pecos valley to Cowles, the road terminus, near which the Pecos Wilderness Area begins. Many excellent trails lead into the high country from Cowles.

Pecos Wilderness

THE WILDERNESS CONCEPT

Most of the area described in this book is part of the Pecos Wilderness Area. The original Pecos Primitive Area, containing 136,000 acres in the Santa Fe National Forest—including, in particular, the upper Pecos drainage basin—was established by the Forest Service in 1933. Several adjustments of boundaries were made later, including the addition of 25,000 acres of the Carson National Forest, north of the Santa Barbara Divide. The enlarged area, 165,000 acres, was designated the Pecos Wilderness in 1955.

What is a Wilderness? The Wilderness Act of 1964 states: "A wilderness, in contrast with those areas where man and his own works dominate the landscape, is hereby recognized as an area where the earth and its community of life are untrammeled by man, where man himself is a visitor who does not remain." An area of wilderness is further defined: ". . . an area of undeveloped Federal land retaining its primeval character and influence, without permanent improvements or human habitation, which is protected and managed so as to preserve its natural conditions and which 1) generally appears to have been affected primarily by the forces of nature, with the imprint of man's work substantially unnoticeable; 2) has outstanding opportunities for solitude or a primitive and unconfined type of recreation; 3) has at least 5,000 acres of land or is of sufficient size to make practicable its preservation and use in an unimpaired condition; and 4) may also contain ecological, geological, or other features of scientific, educational, scenic, or historical value."

Thus large sections of virgin forests, mountains and other wild and remote areas in this country have been set aside for protection as wilderness tracts. Areas of such natural beauty and interest as the Pecos Wilderness are now to be kept inviolate from roads, motorized vehicles, all types of commercial enterprise. Drastic limitations are placed on mineral prospecting, mining and grazing.

In the summer of 1959, while preparing the first edition of this guide book, we traversed all the trails in the upper Pecos area of the Pecos Wilderness. The same was done again in the summer of 1974 in preparation for the present 3rd edition. The greatest changes we noted in this 15-year period have been the major increase in the number of people visiting the Pecos Wilderness each year and a

marked increase of papers and tin cans along the trails. This inexcusable littering is in flagrant disregard of rules of conduct for the Pecos Wilderness Area,
amounting to desecration of its God-given beauty. Those who follow these trails
are asked to honor the trust given them on entering this region; to refrain from
littering and defacing the trees and landscape, and to report all acts of
misconduct to the ranger station in the town of Pecos. Thus each trail rider or
hiker may, in his own way, take a stand in preserving this wilderness "as it was
meant to be."

ENTRANCES TO PECOS WILDERNESS

We suggest visitors obtain a copy of the *Visitor's Guide to the Pecos Wilderness*
from one of the U.S. Forest Service ranger stations (Pecos, Santa Fe, Española,
Peñasco, or Las Vegas). This guide includes a generalized map showing various
entrances to the Wilderness and the upper Pecos.

SOUTH

The most obvious entry to the upper Pecos and the Pecos Wilderness Area is
via NM-63, north from the town of Pecos, up the Pecos River valley to the end of
the highway at Cowles. Numerous campgrounds as well as several guest ranches
are in the Cowles area; many interesting trails radiate from here into the
Wilderness Area. According to Forest Service records, in recent years over 70
percent of the visitors to the Wilderness enter from the Cowles area. At the peak
of the summer season, many of the most popular scenic spots in the upper Pecos
such as Lake Katherine, Pecos Baldy Lake, and Beatty's Flats may be congested
with both hikers and riders.

For those wishing to explore more remote, wilder points of the Pecos
Wilderness where one is better able to find solitude and see a larger variety of
wild animals, we suggest getting off the beaten path. The Santa Barbara Divide,
for example, is much less frequented and provides some of the most spectacular
views in the entire region—as well as the opportunity to examine many features of
geological interest.

We also suggest that the hiker or rider consider using other points of entry into
the Wilderness, in addition to Cowles. The most useful of these are described
below.

WEST

1—The second most popular entry into the upper Pecos is from Santa Fe Ski
Basin (in the Hyde Park area), just northeast of Santa Fe. The trail proceeds
eastward from near the ski lift, connecting with the beginning of the Sky Line
trail and crossing the West Divide between Penitente Peak and Santa Fe Baldy.
By this route, Lake Katherine is only 7 miles from the end of the road.

2—Trails from the Nambé area proceed eastward up Rio Nambé to Panchuela
West and over the divide to Horsethief Meadows, or northeastward, via the head
of Rio Medio, to cross Bordo Lajado south of South Truchas Peak.

3—Panchuela West, Horsethief Meadows, and South Truchas Peak can also be
reached from a trail up Rio Frijoles, beginning near Cundiyo.

4—A trail beginning at the end of the road southeast of Cordova, at the
Borrego Mesa campground, goes up the Rio Medio to Bordo Lajado and South
Truchas Peak.

NORTH

1—The main entry from the north begins at Santa Barbara campground, south of Peñasco. Several trails radiate southward from there into the northern part of the Pecos Wilderness, going up the west, middle, and east forks of the Rio Santa Barbara, and continuing on to connect with Sky Line trail at various points on the Santa Barbara Divide. Trail along the west fork of this river follows one of the most beautiful high-mountain valleys in the entire Pecos Wilderness Area, affording views of many interesting geological features.

2—From the Angostura campground near Tres Ritos, a trail extends southwestward—eventually reaching the Sky Line trail and the Santa Barbara Divide atop Barbara Peak.

EAST

1—From the Cleveland-Mora area a road extends westward several miles up the Rio de la Casa. From the end of the road, a trail extends westward up the Middle Fork of the river, eventually connecting with the Sky Line trail near the east end of Santa Barbara Divide.

2—The most impressive entry to the Pecos Wilderness Area from the east is via the Gascon trail, beginning at Gascon. This trail makes a spectacular, well-graded ascent up the steep east face of the East Divide, reaching the crest of that range and the Sky Line trail at Cebolla Peak, near the head of the southwest-flowing Rio Mora.

3—From Upper Rociada, a main trail climbs the steep face of the East Divide via Sparks Canyon and the Pidlite mine workings, reaching the crest of the divide, and the Sky Line trail, opposite Rito del Oso.

4—From either Gallinas or Porvenir Canyons, northwest of Las Vegas, trails reach the secondary divide between Hollinger and Burro Canyons, connecting with a trail extending westward, past the site of the old Harvey Ranch. Eventually, this trail intersects the Mica Mine road and crosses the East Divide, just north of Elk Mountain, at the point where the Sky Line trail ends.

WILDERNESS PERMIT

A wilderness permit is required of each individual or group entering the Pecos Wilderness Area. The permit is free at the ranger stations in Pecos, Las Vegas, Santa Fe, Española, and Peñasco.

The permit system insures better management of the wilderness area for everyone's benefit. In some locations, sheer numbers of people threaten environmental values and wilderness quality. The permit provides the Forest Service with reliable use data, while at the same time providing an opportunity for one-to-one contact between the wilderness user and the forest ranger to discuss the trip, trail conditions, fire hazards, and location of other visitors. The permit system adds up to a more meaningful and pleasant wilderness experience.

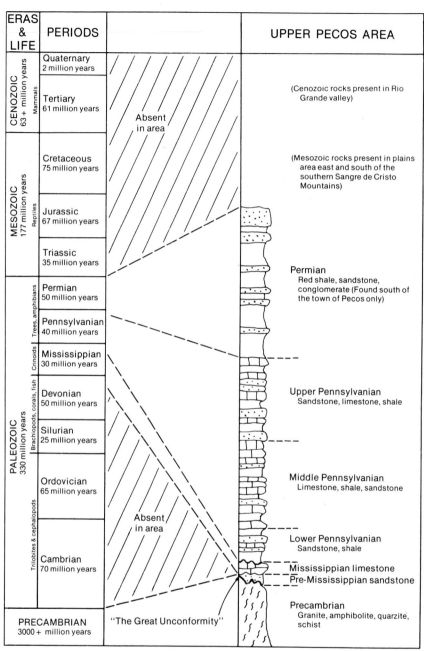

ERAS & LIFE	PERIODS		UPPER PECOS AREA
CENOZOIC 63 + million years — Mammals	Quaternary 2 million years		
	Tertiary 61 million years	Absent in area	(Cenozoic rocks present in Rio Grande valley)
MESOZOIC 177 million years — Reptiles	Cretaceous 75 million years		(Mesozoic rocks present in plains area east and south of the southern Sangre de Cristo Mountains)
	Jurassic 67 million years		
	Triassic 35 million years		
PALEOZOIC 330 million years	Permian 50 million years — Trees, amphibians		Permian Red shale, sandstone, conglomerate (Found south of the town of Pecos only)
	Pennsylvanian 40 million years		
	Mississippian 30 million years — Crinoids		
	Devonian 50 million years — Brachiopods, corals, fish		Upper Pennsylvanian Sandstone, limestone, shale
	Silurian 25 million years		
	Ordovician 65 million years		Middle Pennsylvanian Limestone, shale, sandstone
	Cambrian 70 million years — Trilobites & cephalopods	Absent in area	Lower Pennsylvanian Sandstone, shale
			Mississippian limestone
			Pre-Mississippian sandstone
PRECAMBRIAN 3000 + million years		"The Great Unconformity"	Precambrian Granite, amphibolite, quarzite, schist

GEOLOGIC TIMETABLE.

Geologic History

Descriptions of geologic features along the trails of the upper Pecos region will be more interesting if considered first against the background geologic history of the area, as well as of the entire Rocky Mountain chain—of which this region is a part.

Great mountain systems like the Rockies, despite their immense size and ageless appearance, have not always been where they are now. If one journeys far enough back in geologic time, evidence still present in the rocks tells of periods long before the Rockies came into existence. The present landscape of lofty north-south ridges and deep canyons, typical throughout the upper Pecos country, is actually quite young, geologically speaking, although the time necessary for wearing down and sculpturing even the smallest hills and valleys exceeds a thousand lifetimes. The process geologists call mountain building requires vast eons of time for its operation and final culmination in a chain of lofty peaks. This process still goes on, despite man's inability to observe its effects or understand its ultimate causes.

The Rockies as we know them today did not exist until the end of the Mesozoic Era (geologic timetable, p. 14), roughly 70 million years ago—seemingly a long time, but no more than a relatively short interval in earth history. Certain other mountain systems such as the Appalachians date back far beyond the earliest beginnings of the Rockies. And here and there, rocks found in the Rocky Mountains contain records of still earlier epochs of mountain building and majestic vanished ranges dating back more than a billion years.

These geologic records tell us that in ancient time, in the region now occupied by the upper Pecos River, there were seas in which sediments were deposited and later compacted to thick beds of sandstone, shale, and siltstone. Surface volcanic flows and dikelike intrusive bodies of dark igneous rocks became mixed with the sediments. Then came powerful compressive movements, squeezing the crust from north and south, crumpling the rocks (almost plastic because of their great depth below the surface) into tightly compressed folds. The extreme heat and pressure recrystallized these sedimentary and igneous rocks into such densely crystalline metamorphic equivalents as quartzite, mica schist, and phyllite. Mighty east-west mountain ranges were built up of these metamorphic rocks, and fiery granite magma welled up from subterranean reservoirs to intrude and replace the older rocks while still deep below the surface. The invasion of granite was followed by narrow intrusive dikes of coarse granite pegmatite. Still later, and from the same original magmatic source, came hot silica-bearing solutions infiltrating everywhere and forming abundant quartz veins (which in rare cases are associated with rich concentrations of valuable metallic ores). The zinc-lead-copper deposits of the now-abandoned Pecos mine at Terrero, far up Pecos Canyon, were formed in this way.

Age determinations based on the radioactive decay of such elements as uranium and rubidium present in minerals of certain granite pegmatites of the region have given several ages more than a billion years ago for the time of formation of these pegmatite minerals. These ancient rocks, none showing any evidence of fossils, are included in the Precambrian Era; a vast interval prior to the deposition of the oldest fossiliferous Cambrian rocks of the Paleozoic Era (see geologic timetable).

The intrusion of the Precambrian pegmatite dikes and quartz veins was followed by an immense span of time (close to 600 million years) during which no igneous intrusions nor mountain-building movements, and little or no deposition of sediments occurred in this region. The land surface was above sea level, and the same slow agents of erosion active today—such as running water and wind action—wore down and reduced the elevation of the ancient mountain ranges. Apparently, this area remained above sea level through the early and middle parts of the Paleozoic Era, a span of 200 million years, at a time when various other parts of western North America were periodically submerged.

During or shortly before the beginning of the Mississippian period, 290 million years ago, a sea slowly advanced over the old, eroded, planed-down but still hilly land surface comprised of metamorphic and igneous Precambrian rocks. Among those ancient rocks, the quartzite now composing the Truchas and Chimayosos Peaks, Pecos Baldy, and the walls of the deep canyons near the heads of the Pecos, Valdez, and Mora Rivers formed the highest, most resistant ridges that remained as islands above the shallow, advancing sea. These islands formed an east-west chain in the area between the present-day Truchas Peaks and the head of the Rio Mora, reflecting the original east-west structure of the ancient mountain ranges. Boulders and quartz sands, washed into the sea from these quartzite ridges, were deposited as irregular layers in the shallows near the islands, and later, after compaction, became the clean, light-tan sandstone and conglomerate now seen near Beatty's Flats. These rocks, the oldest sediments resting directly upon the eroded Precambrian surface, cannot be dated precisely because of the absence of fossils. They could be early or middle Paleozoic, or perhaps even early Mississippian. Their distribution and conditions of origin seem closely related to those of the overlying limestones, definitely Mississippian. Hereafter, for simplification, these sandstones of uncertain age will be referred to as pre-Mississippian.

As time passed, limy muds accumulated in the shallow waters near and far from shore, often being deposited directly on those parts of the old Precambrian surface not covered by sand. The scene might well have resembled the broad present-day "lime banks" around the Bahama Islands. In some places, as at Dalton Bluff, the old weathered soil of the Precambrian surface has been preserved by a cover of Mississippian limestones. The thickness of these limestones rarely is more than 100 ft, commonly averaging far less. Occurring as a distinctive, irregularly bedded sequence of massive light-gray rocks forming prominent cliffs, these beds thin northward and are totally absent in some parts of the upper Pecos region.

Following deposition of Mississippian limestones, the region was slowly elevated above sea level and exposed once again to erosional processes, but only for a relatively short interval compared to the vast eons of time between the end of the Precambrian and the beginning of the Mississippian. Then in early Pennsylvanian time the region subsided, allowing the sea to readvance across the now somewhat irregular land surface. Mississippian limestone was exposed over that surface in many areas, but the old Precambrian rocks were exposed in others where the Mississippian rocks had either been completely eroded away or never deposited.

Most of the sedimentary rocks in the Pecos high country are Pennsylvanian. They have a total thickness of about 2,700 ft north of the town Pecos. The thickness is highly irregular, however, reaching as much as 8,000 ft some 20 miles north. These rocks were first deposited in the form of unconsolidated sediments (sands, muds, and limy deposits) under a great variety of rapidly fluctuating conditions, during which sea level changed many times, advancing and retreating across the region time and time again.

These unconsolidated sediments were then cemented and compacted during burial beneath later overlying sediments, to form the highly varied sandstones, shales, and limestones now seen in many parts of the upper Pecos. Some represent nonmarine river and alluvial deposits, as in the case of those coarse, poorly sorted sandstones sometimes containing land plants. Others represent marine deposits, exemplified by the limestones and dark-gray shales. These latter types often contain abundant marine invertebrate fossils, such as brachiopods, corals, bryozoans, gastropods, pelecypods, and fusulinids (see glossary).

In the Pecos valley, the Early Pennsylvanian sequence, having originated chiefly under nonmarine depositional conditions (in this paper Early Pennsylvanian is used to include the Morrowan and Atokan Epochs, Middle Pennsylvanian to include the Desmoinesian Epoch, and Late Pennsylvanian to include the Missourian and Virgilian Epochs), is represented by a thickness of about 400 ft of sandstones and shales, together with some coal lenses and minor, thin beds of limestone. Marine depositional conditions characterized Middle Pennsylvanian time, when a sea covered the area again and again. Typically, the resultant rock types are thick units composed of thin, nodular limestones alternating with black shales, which in turn alternate with thinner beds of nonmarine sandstone. The total thickness of Middle Pennsylvanian rocks of this region is about 1,200 ft.

During Late Pennsylvanian time, the area was covered by the sea less frequently; thus, the resultant rock types found in the upper Pecos area are relatively rare: marine limestones alternating with thick, nonmarine sandstones and shales. Total thickness of Upper Pennsylvanian rocks now found in the Pecos valley region is about 1,100 ft.

The Permian period that followed was marked in this region by withdrawal of the sea to the south and by arid conditions. The thick, dark-red shales and lenticular sandstones of the Pecos area (also seen on the sides of Glorieta Mesa) were probably deposited on sun-baked mud flats occasionally crossed by channels partly filled with sand. Iron-stained red beds hundreds of feet thick accumulated in this manner.

Rocks of Mesozoic age, although not present in the upper Pecos region, are found in the plains region east and southeast of the mountains. Near the end of the Mesozoic era, some 130 million years after the close of the Permian period, the tremendous forces that culminated in the formation of the Rocky Mountains slowly crumpled the earth's crust along a north-south axis, causing the rocks to be arched up into great folds, overturned to the east, and then broken along extensive faults.

In the upper Pecos region, the arched-up anticlinal folds, as well as the uplift along certain fault dislocations, tended to bring up the deeper lying oldest Precambrian rocks to a higher level. Synclinal downwarping folds, together with subsidence along some faults, did just the opposite, leaving the old crystalline rocks buried beneath great thicknesses of Paleozoic sediments. Today such differential crustal movements have their aftermath in the elevated positions of Precambrian rocks in the highest peaks of the area, and in the thick cover of Pennsylvanian sediments bordering so much of the Pecos valley between Dalton campground and Cowles.

Mighty crustal disturbances, such as those culminating in the formation of the Rocky Mountains, do not happen quickly. Such major earth processes, called orogenic revolutions, are concentrated along lines of weakness in the crust and take place over millions of years in countless small-scale movements repeated over and over again. The final result of such a gradual, slow-moving process is the formation of a gigantic mountain chain like the Rockies. Earthquakes occurring in many parts of the world today are due to similar small-scale crustal movements and give evidence that major orogenic forces, the same as those responsible for the high mountain terrain of the upper Pecos country, are continuing today.

Following uplift of the Rocky Mountains, the upper Pecos region was never again submerged beneath sea level. Weathering and erosion gradually stripped away the rock exposed at the surface and reduced the elevation of the mountains. Rushing torrents like the present-day Pecos and Mora Rivers slowly wore through the cover of Paleozoic sedimentary rocks, and along the deeper canyons especially, cut deeply into the ancient Precambrian rocks beneath.

During Cenozoic time, low-lying areas at the base of the uplifted ranges, such as the extensive area now marking the valley of the Rio Grande between the Sangre de Cristo Range and the westerly Jemez Mountains, became partly filled with unconsolidated sand, silt, and gravel washed down from the Sangre de Cristo Mountains over millions of years. Today these deposits forming the dissected foothills along the west slope of the Sangre de Cristo Mountains can be seen in many roadcuts along US-64 between Santa Fe and Taos.

More recently (ending about 12,000 years ago), when most of North America was covered with great sheets of ice, glaciation was extensive in the upper Pecos region: the higher peaks of the area all contained small valley glaciers, and the present jagged character of the topmost summits of the upper Pecos high country is a result of the long-continued scraping and sculpturing action of glacial ice.

How to Use Geology and Trail Map

The geology and trail map (in pocket) graphically shows some results of field work in the area covered by this trail guide. Its chief aim, with respect to the geologic data, is to present an accurate, simplified picture of the geology of the upper Pecos region. All explanations of geologic features in the text are based on the findings incorporated into this map.

DISTRIBUTION OF ROCKS

Each color or color pattern on this map indicates a particular rock type located in the surface exposures. The various colors and color patterns thus show the surface distribution of all rocks in this part of the Sangre de Cristo region. After such geologic mapping is completed, rock outcrops can be correlated and a stratigraphic, or rock-sequence, column constructed showing the order of age from oldest (at the bottom) to the youngest (at the top). In the explanation at the right of the map, such a stratigraphic column is given, with the colors appropriate to each rock type.

The map, in general, has two main colors representing the two major rock types present in the upper Pecos region. One of these types comprises the younger (and therefore stratigraphically higher) sedimentary bedded rocks of Paleozoic age (blue). The second includes the underlying ancient metamorphic and igneous Precambrian rocks (red).

PALEOZOIC ROCKS (blue)

The two Paleozoic patterns on the map are:

1) Older Mississippian rocks, forming a relatively thin unit, usually appear as a narrow band on the map. They typically consist of gray limestones. Still older pre-Mississippian sandstones, locally present at the base of the Mississippian, are included also in this thin map unit.

2) Younger Pennsylvanian rocks total hundreds of feet in thickness and are mostly tan to gray sandstones, dark-gray shales, and nodular gray limestones. These rocks occupy the higher slopes of most canyons and the summit areas of almost all flat-topped and smoothly-sculptured ridges.

PRECAMBRIAN ROCKS (red)

The second major rock type consists of the very old Precambrian rocks of great variety and complexity, commonly without bedding, but tending to be massive, slabby, or micaceous. These rocks are densely crystalline and extremely tough, and thus resist weathering; where typically found in the bottoms of the deeper canyons, they form steep cliffs and narrow box canyons. In certain areas also, through uplift by faulting or folding, they may stand high above the surrounding country to form towering peaks whose resistant summit ridges have been carved by now-vanished glaciers into rugged, serrate shapes.

The following Precambrian rock types are dominant in the area:

1) Black amphibolite and tan to pink granite (p. 31) form the lower parts of the deep canyons along the Pecos River south of Cowles and northeast from there to the upper Rio Mora. Granite also makes up the Santa Fe Range (West Divide).

2) Gray to glassy-white quartzite forms the Truchas Peaks, Pecos Baldy, and Chimayosos Peak, as well as the lofty white cliffs bordering the upper, northern parts of the canyons of the Pecos and Mora Rivers.

3) Less commonly, narrow zones of softer, slabby, micaceous schists and phyllites occur mixed with the quartzite. Good exposures are found for a short distance northeast of Beatty's Flats along the upper Pecos River and along sections of the upper Rio Mora.

GEOLOGIC STRUCTURES

After mapping the distribution of rocks at the surface and looking for a meaningful pattern and directional trends for scattered occurrences of the same rock types, the geologist tries to work out the three-dimensional rock structure from the surface downward. Cross sections constructed to scale, like vertical slices cut downward from the surface, are especially helpful in portraying regional geology. Several such diagrams appear in the text on pages 35, 54, and 79, and the surface location of two other cross sections (A and B) are shown on the geology and trail map.

THE "GREAT UNCONFORMITY"

Contacts between different rock formations are shown on the map by thin black lines. One such contact, more than all others, is extraordinarily significant. This line on the map separating the two main colors, blue and red, is the contact between the overlying bedded Paleozoic rocks and the underlying, massive, igneous and metamorphic Precambrian rocks. This contact signifies a profound gap in time, encompassing some 600 million years—a missing interval marked by a tremendously long period of surface erosion during which great mountain ranges became worn down to a fairly flat, though hilly, land surface. Such a contact, representing a vast time break, is called an unconformity.

How can one be sure of the immense time represented by this unconformity and the long-continued erosional effects, when the Paleozoic rocks are lying in direct contact with and upon the Precambrian rocks? The following points summarize the main evidence:

1) Certain of the youngest Precambrian igneous rocks have been dated by radioactive-decay measurements, and the upper Paleozoic beds have been dated relatively by the fossils they contain (see p. 29).

2) The original characteristics of many of the Precambrian rocks have been altered by heat and pressure and by mighty deforming forces deep in the crust to yield the metamorphosed (wholly changed) densely crystalline rocks they are now. In contrast, the overlying Paleozoic rocks have been relatively unmetamorphosed and still show their sedimentary character.

3) Wherever original sedimentary bedding in the Precambrian can be detected, its usual attitude is found to be strongly tilted, commonly steeply inclined to almost vertical, in striking contrast to the almost typically flat Paleozoic beds lying above the contact (diagram, p. 79).

4) Striking topographic irregularities of hills and valleys, scores of feet high and deep, occur along the contact surface. There are also, here and there on this surface, preserved remnants of an ancient weathered soil. Such criteria are unmistakable evidence of long-continued erosional effects; obviously the rocks must have been lifted up above sea level and exposed to weathering for vast periods of time.

Once you learn to recognize the "great unconformity" along the roads and trails of the upper Pecos region, and become familiar with the far-reaching geologic concept represented, a better understanding of all aspects of the regional geology is possible.

FOLDS

Folds are the result of either crustal compressional forces or of huge crustal dislocations tending to shove rocks together and bend them upward and downward into archlike folds (anticlines) and troughlike folds (synclines). The geologic map shows two major folds in this area, located on the map by two long, dashed, north-south lines. These lines mark the centers (axes) of the folds, and can be identified on the map by their inward-pointing arrows (syncline) and outward-pointing arrows (anticline). The small strike-and-dip symbols (✕) on the map also help to show the locations of folds. These symbols show, by the number of angular degrees given in each case, the inclination or tilt of sedimentary beds. The longer line in the symbol indicates the strike, or direction of horizontal trend of the bedding strata. The short line of the symbol, perpendicular to the strike line, gives the angular dip, or tilt, in the direction of inclination of the bedding. Just a few of the hundreds of strike-and-dip symbols on the larger geologic map of much of the southernmost Sangre de Cristo region appear on this small version in the trail guide.

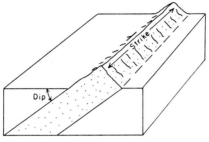

STRIKE AND DIP.

One of the two major folds mentioned earlier is a north-south syncline near the westerly edge of the Paleozoic rocks where they contact adjacent granite. On either side of the synclinal axis, strike-dip symbols in the bedded Pennsylvanian rocks show these beds to be dipping downward from both east and west toward this axis, marking the lowest central position of the fold. This syncline, running parallel to the Pecos River and several miles west of it for a north-south distance of at least 10 miles, plunges (or inclines) gently to the south. The arrow at the south end of the syncline axis points in the direction of plunge. Evidence of the southward plunge of this syncline is seen in the general southerly dip of Paleozoic beds in the area around the town of Pecos and northward along the Pecos River.

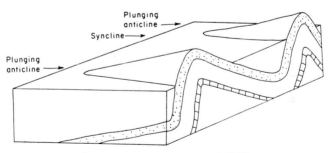

PLUNGING ANTICLINES AND SYNCLINE.

East of the Pecos River, the map shows increasingly broad outcrops of Precambrian rocks, almost to the top of the East Divide north of Elk Mountain. This is controlled by the presence of a long north-south anticlinal fold that arches up the deep-lying Precambrian rocks near the center of the anticline to expose these at much higher levels. The overlying Paleozoic beds in this area are left only along the loftiest ridge summits. This anticline is located on the map by a long north-south axial line with associated arrows pointing outward, instead of inward as in the case of the syncline. The arrow at the south end of the axis points south to show a gentle southward plunge similar to that of the syncline. This great anticline is highly asymmetrical. The west limb slopes gently down towards the Pecos valley. The steep, locally vertical or overturned east limb has been mostly re-moved by erosion but is locally preserved in the foothills east of the mountains, particularly on the ridge between Beaver and Hollinger Creeks (geology and trail map).

The southward plunge of the major north-south folds deeply submerges the underlying Precambrian rocks below the surface in the neighborhood of the town of Pecos. Inasmuch as the high peaks of the Rockies are supported mostly by resistant Precambrian rocks, the absence of such resistant rocks at the surface south of the town of Pecos has allowed erosion to wear down the overlying, less resistant sedimentary rocks to relatively low, flat surfaces—one reason why the Rockies finally play out in the vicinity of the town of Pecos.

FAULTS

Several heavy black lines are shown on the map; these represent major faults, or huge crustal breaks, as if the crust had been cut through vertically with a knife for long distances. Along such dislocation surfaces, rocks have been shifted upward hundreds of feet on one side relative to a similar downward displacement on the other (diagram p. 79).

Inasmuch as such widespread movement disrupts rocks that originally belonged together and separates the similar parts hundreds of feet upward and downward, these faults will tend (in the larger dislocations at least) to bring into contact at the surface, as well as on the map, rocks of entirely different age and character. Such contacts will appear abnormal in terms of the rock contacts normally found throughout the mapped region, until clarified satisfactorily in terms of the faulting that produced them. The best example of such a contact anomaly, explainable solely in terms of faulting, is the widespread north-south contact of Early and Middle Pennsylvanian bedded rocks with Precambrian granite near the west side of the map. Normally these particular Pennsylvanian beds, accurately dated by means of their fossils, occur 1,000 to 2,000 ft above the Precambrian.

This particular fault, separating Pennsylvanian rocks from Precambrian granite, runs in a north-south direction across the entire map. Geologic mapping has traced this same fault another 20 miles northward; southward it runs for an additional 5 to 10 miles to the south end of the Precambrian rocks (southern terminus of the Rockies) in the vicinity of Glorieta Baldy, west of the town of Pecos. Detailed mapping of the Precambrian rocks that lie in direct contact along a small portion of the fault indicates that this huge crustal dislocation may well date back into Precambrian time, and that its earliest displacement was a lateral one of miles-long magnitude along a north-south direction. As so commonly happens, the original lateral (strike-slip) faulting opened up an extensive north-south zone of weakness in the crust. More recent movement, this time up-and-down (normal fault), has followed that original line of weakness to cause the almost vertical displacement of rocks now found in the area. That this later faulting occurred in post-Pennsylvanian time is proved by the fact that Pennsylvanian beds have been displaced and dropped downward against the fault long after they were first deposited as sediments in Pennsylvanian time, and even long after they were eventually consolidated into solid rock.

Two other faults are shown on the map. The one swinging northeastward around the Truchas Peaks is a major fault along which very steep up-and-down movement has taken place in post-Pennsylvanian time. This fault separates Precambrian quartzite from Pennsylvanian rocks to the east. Pennsylvanian beds are vertical along some parts of this fault. Along this major dislocation the tough Precambrian quartzite responsible for upholding the lofty summits of Truchas Peaks has been uplifted. The third fault, near Cowles, is a minor normal fault along which a 100-ft vertical displacement of the Mississippian limestone beds can be observed. The vertical movements along the two major faults just discussed probably occurred about 70 million years ago during that long-continued period of great crustal disturbances called the Laramide Revolution. The small fault at Cowles could be more recent.

PLATE 1

Photo
Gallery

SOUTH TRUCHAS PEAK
From lowermost of Truchas Lakes.

PLATE 2

SOUTH AND MIDDLE TRUCHAS PEAKS
View from south slope of Chimayosos Peak and Sky Line trail.

BLUE COLUMBINES
Rocky east slope of South Truchas Peak, along Sky Line trail.

PLATE 3

NORTH TRUCHAS PEAK

HIGH MOUNTAIN MEADOW WITH RED PRIMROSES
Pecos Baldy and Bordo Lajado on skyline.

PLATE 4

LATE SPRING SNOWS LINGER ON TRUCHAS PEAKS
View from north part Hamilton Mesa.

PECOS RIVER VALLEY
View north towards Beatty's Flats from high cliffs above Pecos Canyon.

PLATE 5

CHIMAYOSOS PEAK FROM SANTA BARBARA DIVIDE
Trace of major fault separates white Precambrian quartzite (top of peak) from folded
Pennsylvanian sedimentary rocks.

RIO SANTA BARBARA, WEST FORK
Looking north towards Taos Range. Major fault separates Precambrian quartzite cliffs
on west (at left) from less rugged Pennsylvanian sedimentary strata on east.

PLATE 6

RIO SANTA BARBARA, WEST FORK
View south to Chimayosos Peak.

VIEW SOUTHEAST FROM GASCON POINT
Rociada Valley and Hermit's Peak in distance.

PLATE 7

CEBOLLA PEAK AND THE EAST RANGE
View from east, from Gascon.

MIDDLE AND NORTH TRUCHAS PEAKS
View from summit of South Truchas Peak. Taos Range on distant skyline.

PLATE 8

PECOS FALLS
Flowing over jointed Precambrian quartzite.

Trip Logs
and Trail Guides

Trip 1

HIGHWAY 63—PECOS TO COWLES

A settlement since the early 1700's, the town of Pecos (altitude 6,900 ft; population 600), named for the famous river bordering the town, is dominantly Spanish-American in character. The old part of town, clustered around the church, is located just south of where Pecos valley changes from a broad river flat to a narrow canyon. The legendary Santa Fe Trail, first opened in 1792, passed nearby, between the town and Glorieta Mesa.

Two miles south are the ruins of the once-great Pecos Pueblo. When the first Spanish expedition, under Coronado, visited the area in 1540 in search of the Seven Cities of Gold, this was the largest, most thriving of all Indian pueblos, with an estimated population of 3,000. Although the pueblo prospered until about 1720, by 1750 the population had dwindled, owing to sickness and raids by Comanches from the eastern plains. In 1768 a smallpox epidemic left only 180 survivors. In 1838 the few remaining inhabitants migrated to Jemez Pueblo, where the same language was spoken. The abandoned pueblo fell rapidly into decay—a process aided by those traveling the Santa Fe Trail who tore out the pueblo beams for firewood. In 1869 the beams of the large adobe church, rebuilt in the early 1700's by Spanish missionaries, were removed and used as corral posts; afterwards, the unprotected walls gradually disintegrated. Parts of the 6-ft-thick adobe church walls are still standing, however, and today the site is a National Monument open to the public. The ruins have been partly excavated by archaeologists, with some reconstruction to depict how the Pecos Indians lived in this extensive communal center 500 years ago. From time to time, descendants of the Pecos Pueblo Indians living at Jemez return to the ruins with ceremonial offerings of cornmeal.

The hills surrounding Pecos are composed of Permian red and maroon shales and sandstones stained by iron oxide. Looking south from Pecos towards the broad mass of Glorieta Mesa (photograph), you look forward in geologic time, for beds of sedimentary rocks in the area dip gently southward, lying stratigraphically higher—thus becoming geologically younger—in that direction. Up the Pecos valley north from Pecos, the Permian red beds are left behind, and the underlying older gray, tan, and pink Late Pennsylvanian limestones, sandstones, and shales are encountered.

The earliest geological observations at the town of Pecos were made in 1853 by Jules Marcou, a geologist from Switzerland with a U.S. Army expedition searching for a possible railway route across the continent near the 35th parallel. Marcou's geological map, published in 1858, shows his route and campsites. He camped for one night on the bank of the Pecos River, at the sharp bend in the stream about three-quarters of a mile west of where NM-63 crosses the river at the north edge of town.

Pecos River, which flows generally southward, is locally deflected in this area for about a mile by a small east-west-trending ridge of resistant layers of Upper Pennsylvanian limestone (crossed by the highway at mile 0.8 on road log).

0.0   Trip begins in the town of Pecos at the intersection of NM-50 and NM-63. Take NM-63 north, toward the mountains.

0.6   St. Anthony's Church, to right.

0.8   The contact between Permian red shales and sandstones and Pennsyl-

GLORIETA MESA.
View south from Pecos Pueblo National Monument.

vanian gray limestones is poorly exposed on left side of highway, at the south side of the east-west-trending ridge of limestone.

0.9 Bridge over Pecos River. The broad, open valley of Pecos River, south of the town of Pecos, narrows to the north here, with sharp bluffs of resistant beds of massive Late Pennsylvanian limestones and sandstones along the river on either side. Gentle southward dip of these strata is apparent in the high bluff to the left of the bridge, where sparse fossils, such as brachiopods and fusulinids, can be collected. These fossils serve to date the beds as Late Pennsylvanian.

1.4 Sharp curve; Benedictine monastery on left was formerly the well-known Valley (dude) ranch. For the next mile and a half, roadcuts and river bluffs are composed of beds of Late Pennsylvanian limestone, sandstone, conglomerate, and shale.

2.7 State trout hatchery. Many streams and lakes of the upper Pecos region are stocked from this hatchery. Prominent bluff behind the hatchery is Middle Pennsylvanian chert and limestone. As road continues north up the canyon, keep in mind that the rocks become increasingly older because of the southward tilt of the beds.

4.3 Canyon opens, giving a fine view northward far up the broad valley. Large house ahead, with high-pitched roof and massive stone chimney, was designed by the famous architect, Frank Lloyd Wright.

4.5 After passing Santa Fe National Forest sign and stone monument on right, look back southward toward a sharp, triangular hill in the center of the valley. This hill is formed by cliffs of Middle Pennsylvanian limestone, shales, and sandstones whose beds dip gently to the southwest. The river turns sharply eastward around the northeast face of this hill. An earlier

PECOS VALLEY.
Looking north from point 4.3 miles north of the town of Pecos.

course of the river probably followed the now-dry arroyo between this hill
and the high cliffs to the west.

5.1   Road to left leads to the small Spanish-American settlement of Lower
La Pasada (The Pass). This name appears incorrectly on the U.S. Geological Survey 7½-minute topographic map as Lower La Posada (The Inn).

5.6   In the middle of the high cliffs on the west side of the canyon is a large
landslide. Dark mine dumps nearby evidence early attempts to extract
thin seams of Early Pennsylvanian bituminous coal. (The great coal
deposits of the northern Appalachians, that made possible the industrial
development of much of the Eastern United States, are Pennsylvanian,
as are most high-grade coal deposits of the world.)

6.4   Sign: "Dalton fishing site." On the west side of the canyon is a towering
cliff exposing one of the key geologic outcrops of the upper Pecos region.
This cliff is geologically important because many different sedimentary
layers occur atop one another in one fully exposed series. Here the entire
lower half of the Pennsylvanian sequence found in the upper Pecos region
is present, consisting of a pile of about 1,200 ft of sedimentary beds. Hard
limestone layers jut out as sharp cliffs, whereas soft shales and siltstones
mark the more gentle slopes.

Stratigraphers and paleontologists have scaled this cliff face to measure
the thicknesses of individual beds and to collect and study the fossil assemblages found in certain of the strata. Each fossiliferous bed represents a particular association of marine animals living together in sea

water at a certain depth, under certain environmental conditions, and represents an evolutionary development of a certain limited time episode of earth history. Therefore, fossil assemblages collected from the lower part of Dalton Bluff are different from those in the middle or upper parts. Some species lived for a limited time only, dying before deposition of succeeding layers. Thus, where many fossiliferous layers are exposed in orderly sequence, a known series of fossil assemblages may be established for reference throughout a region. Consequently, an experienced paleontologist can examine an isolated fossiliferous bed in some other part of the upper Pecos country, and date and correlate it with this known sequence.

As a result of such fossil and stratigraphic studies, paleontologists have been able to construct an almost complete stratigraphic column for the entire earth, commencing with the earliest richly fossiliferous beds (the Cambrian) at the beginning of the Paleozoic era, and extending upward to the relatively recent Cenozoic formations (geologic timetable, p. 14).

The massive limestone cliffs halfway up Dalton Bluff are particularly fossiliferous: some limestone and gray shale layers contain, among other fossils, many well-preserved brachiopods, corals, and fusulinids.

In the lowest part of Dalton Bluff is a relatively thin sequence of about 100 ft of Mississippian limestones, distinctively different in appearance from the overlying Pennsylvanian strata. These limestones are light gray, irregularly bedded, massive, and cliff-forming. They rarely contain fossils, possibly because of adverse environmental conditions during the time of deposition.

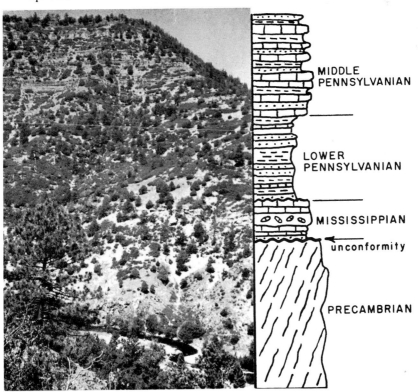

MIDDLE PENNSYLVANIAN

LOWER PENNSYLVANIAN

MISSISSIPPIAN

unconformity

PRECAMBRIAN

DALTON BLUFF.

BRACHIOPOD.
Neospirifer.

Below the Mississippian limestone, near the edge of the river, are cliffs of a dark, massive, highly resistant Precambrian rock. The irregular contact (unconformity) between this rock and the overlying limestone represents a vast time gap (p. 15). Such dark, commonly fine-grained Precambrian rocks are called amphibolite, because of the black amphibole mineral, hornblende, prominently present along with gray plagioclase feldspar. These originated as basic igneous rocks, consisting either of thick flows of volcanic basalt or dikelike intrusive bodies of diabase. Farther north along the canyon, a tan to pinkish coarse-grained granite, largely made up of light-colored quartz and alkalic feldspar, is closely associated with the amphibolite. The granite, also igneous in origin, is younger than the amphibolite, shown by exposures of the contact between the two rocks near the mouth of Indian Creek, 5 miles to the north. There, the molten granite ate its way into the older amphibolite, cutting off and incorporating bits of the dark rock to create a dark, spotted granite near the contact. These two rocks, tan to pink granite and gray-black amphibolite, are the two main Precambrian rock units present throughout the deeper parts of Pecos Canyon and its major tributaries, from Dalton Canyon northward past Cowles.

Across the bridge over Pecos River at Dalton, steep cliffs of dark Precambrian amphibolite rise above east bank of river ahead. Note the far more rugged topography developed in these resistant crystalline rocks, in contrast with the more open, gentle slopes eroded from the sedimentary beds overlying the Precambrian contact southward in the canyon. Inasmuch as this rugged topography characterizes most of the larger canyon bottoms from here north, the Paleozoic-Precambrian unconformity must be a surface that rises northward in elevation, as do the beds above it; otherwise, as the canyon ascends northward, the canyon bottom would only cut into rocks progressively higher above the contact and never extend below it. This general southerly dip of the Precambrian surface is modified locally by undulations representing actual hills and valleys buried during deposition of later formations on top of the unconformity. These irregularities increased in magnitude through later folding of the rocks of this area.

8.6   Macho Church. This Spanish church dates back perhaps 100 years to the time of the earliest settlers along the upper Pecos River. Note that the "great unconformity" (p. 20) is several hundred feet higher on the east side of the canyon than it is immediately above the church on the west side. This difference in elevation is caused by a 10-degree southwestward dip of the contact surface here.

10.1   "Windy Bridge" National Forest picnic ground near bridge over Pecos River.

10.6   About half a mile past bridge over Pecos River, great cliffs of tan granite rise vertically 500 ft above the highway. The "great unconformity," together with the directly overlying Mississippian limestone beds that were seen 50 ft above the Pecos River at Dalton Bluff, now lies fully 800 ft above the river.

11.1   Indian Creek Lodge. The abandoned Johnny Jones copper mine, located 5 miles west, is near the head of the south fork of Indian Creek.

13.7   Bridge. Road to left goes 3 miles up Holy Ghost Canyon, where many summer homes have been built. From a large Forest Service campground at the end of this road, a trail leads northwest, giving access to the western part of the Pecos Wilderness and the high peaks and other points of interest on the West (Santa Fe) Divide (Trip 11).

13.9   After crossing bridge over Pecos River, road reaches the store and post office at Terrero (7,680 ft). ("Tererro" is a corruption or misspelling of the Spanish word "terrero" meaning mound, dump, place for mine waste.) The original post office was located at the Pecos mine, about a mile and a half farther up the valley. Pavement ends here.

Bluffs on west side of river contain excellent exposures of Mississippian limestone, now at river level once again. The cave in this limestone cliff opposite the post office figures prominently in Pecos Pueblo Indian legends, and was reportedly used for important ceremonial rites during the Pueblo

MACHO CHURCH.
View north up Pecos valley.

TERERRO POST OFFICE.
Indian cave visible in Mississippian limestone cliffs across Pecos River.

occupation. This may be the cave Willa Cather refers to (p. 117-136) in her novel, *Death Comes for the Archbishop.*

15.1   Small dump on left side of road marks point from which the aerial tramway from the now-abandoned Pecos mine was suspended over the canyon to the top of the cliffs on the west side (downstream). Day and night for 10 years this tramway carried ore 12 miles south to the flotation mill in Alamitos Canyon just west of the town of Pecos.

15.6   Dumps of the abandoned Pecos mine and Willow Creek campground administered by the New Mexico Department of Game and Fish. Road to the right follows eastward up the south fork of Willow Creek to East (Elk Mountain) Divide, Trip 10. At one time, the Pecos mine was one of the largest zinc-lead-copper mines of the Southwest. This rich deposit was known as far back as the 1880's, but large-scale mining did not commence until 1925, when the American Metal Co. (now American Metal Climax, Inc.) took over the property. Thereupon, an aerial tramway was constructed (the longest of its kind in the world at the time), the mill west of Pecos was built, and ore was mined and milled at the rate of 700 tons a day. Two shafts, one more than 1,000 ft deep, were put down on two separate ore zones, the Evangeline (east) and the Katydid (west), consisting of flat-lenticular, vertically disposed bodies of sulfide minerals up to 50-ft wide, and extending more than a quarter of a mile northeast in the Precambrian amphibolite. The mine was abandoned in the late 1930's, when the combined problems of deep-level mining, pumping out large volumes of water, and labor disputes all became insurmountable.

The dumps are spread out above the road south of Willow Creek for a quarter of a mile. On rare occasions, badly weathered chunks of the chief ore minerals, brownish-black sphalerite (zinc sulfide), silvery galena (lead sulfide), and brassy chalcopyrite (copper and iron sulfide) can be found. Good specimens of pyrite cubes (iron sulfide) in a gray micaceous rock, and

DUMPS OF PECOS MINE.
Looking towards Pecos valley from point above Willow Creek.

slender, black prismatic crystals of tourmaline (boron aluminum silicate) in gray-green schist can be collected here (with a little searching and luck). Gold and silver also occurred in the ore. The richer ore carried 16 percent zinc, 4 percent lead, 1 percent copper, 3 ounces of silver to the ton, and 0.1 ounce of gold to the ton—an ore of high value. The total ore mined and milled may well have exceeded 1.5 million tons. With few rich mines in this region, you wonder what unique circumstances conspired to bring about the concentration in this one small area of such huge tonnages of rare and valuable metals. The answer will never be known with certainty, but economic geologists are fairly sure that such concentrations of rare metals must have originated during Precambrian time, from a source related to the deep-seated intrusive granite magma. Geologic evidence also clearly indicates that all the surrounding rocks were mashed and shattered, and these fractured and permeable rocks became flooded with hot, water-rich, silica-bearing solutions born from the final crystallizing stages of a cooling, deep-seated granitic magma. All granitic rocks contain traces of rare metallic elements; but only by a series of special controlling factors acting together at the right time to concentrate and reconcentrate such bare traces of those elements into solutions that could carry them into the shattered and open rocks, could such an extraordinary geologic phenomenon have occurred. Such problems keep geologists awake at night, but such problems also make geology an ever-challenging and fascinating science.

At the entrance to one of the old tunnels (VERY DANGEROUS!) above the mine dumps on the north side of Willow Creek Canyon, is an

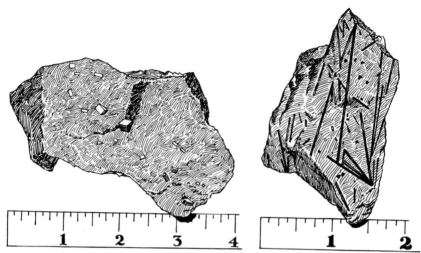

PYRITE CUBES IN SCHIST; TOURMALINE PRISMS IN SCHIST (*scale in inches*).

especially fine exposure of the "great unconformity." Almost flat-lying Mississippian limestone beds rest directly on the ancient erosion surface cut into dark, mineralized amphibolite of Precambrian age beneath (photo, below). In some places exposed underground in the tunnels, unmineralized limestone was found resting directly on weathered and oxidized ore. Such evidence proves the time of ore formation was pre-Mississippian, and most probably Precambrian.

17.1   Bridge over Mora River, one of the best-known trout streams of the upper Pecos region. Several excellent campgrounds administered by the New Mexico Department of Game and Fish are along this section of the highway.

18.0   Fine view of Pecos Baldy far up canyon to north, soon after the highway climbs high above the river. Pecos Baldy is 8 miles away (as the crow

THE "GREAT UNCONFORMITY."
Exposure at entrance to abandoned mine tunnel.

PECOS VALLEY NEAR COWLES.
View north from Los Pinos guest ranch.

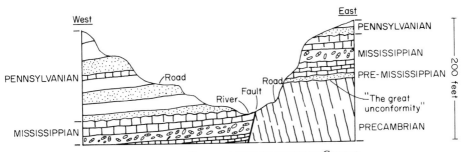

CROSS SECTION OF PECOS VALLEY JUST NORTH OF COWLES.

flies), but appears much closer! Far below the road, the steep canyon bottom is cut deep into massive Precambrian amphibolite.

18.7   Road to right leads around the high north slope of Grass Mountain, north along the ridge toward the beginning of Hamilton Mesa. At 1.2 miles a trail separates, leading to the top of Grass Mountain (introduction to Trip 2), and at 3.0 miles a trail leads to lower Mora Canyon (Trip 9). After 4.2 miles, the road ends at Iron Gate campground, at the edge of the Pecos Wilderness. This campground is the starting point for much-traveled trails leading to Beatty's, Pecos Falls, and upper Mora River (Trips 2, 3, and 8).

19.1   Road begins descent toward Cowles. Prominent Mississippian limestone cliffs on west bank of river.

19.7   Road to right, immediately past rock cliffs of Precambrian amphibolite, goes up east side of Pecos valley for three-quarters of a mile; then up Jacks Creek Valley to Jacks Creek campground. The campground and corrals, administered by the Forest Service, are the largest in the upper Pecos area; and are located near the south boundary of the Wilderness Area. The campground begins 2.4 miles north of the road junction at Cowles and extends over half a mile along the valley. The lower campground is the beginning point for the much-used trail up Round Mountain to Beatty's

(Trip 4) and Pecos Baldy Lake (Trip 5). The trail from Cowles to Hamilton Mesa, via Geronimo's ranch, crosses Jacks Creek road 0.8 mile north of Cowles (Trip 2).

Immediately past road junction, Cowles general store and Mountain View guest ranch (8,200 ft).

19.8 Cross bridge to left, over Pecos River, past store.

Pecos River, which runs straight north for a mile past Cowles, follows a fault. Along this fault, the Mississippian limestone beds are dropped 100 ft lower on the west side of the valley; on this side, they lie closer to the river level than on the east side, where they form a prominent bluff 100 ft above the river. The top of these limestone beds west of the fault can be observed in the river bed a quarter of a mile upstream from the general store, opposite Los Pinos guest ranch. The valley side on the west, where the road to Panchuela is located, is composed of Lower Pennsylvanian sandstones and shales, occasionally seen in small exposures along the road northward. The best exposures of Lower Pennsylvanian in the Cowles area are in the large road cuts on the road to Jacks Creek campground.

19.9 Road junction, NM-63 ends. Both roads beyond this point are Forest Service roads. Side road straight ahead along creek to west, up Winsor Canyon, leads 1 mile to Forest Service campground and to starting points of trails to Lake Katherine, Santa Fe Baldy, and other points of interest on the West Range (Trips 12, 13). Road continuing up Pecos valley turns right up steep hill.

20.2 Los Pinos ranch on right.

20.4 Road to right descends to summer houses near Pecos River.

21.1 Panchuela Ranger Station on right. Trail signpost on hillside above road, on left, opposite gate; trail starts here for Cave Creek and Horsethief Meadows (Trip 14) and for Pecos Baldy Lake, via Dockwiller trail over Mystery Ridge (Trip 6).

21.3 Highway ends at Panchuela forest service campground, on Panchuela Creek, a tributary of Pecos River. Trail, marked by sign, leads across bridge over creek, and connects upstream with trail to Horsethief Meadows and Pecos Baldy Lake.

Trip 2

HAMILTON MESA TRAIL— COWLES TO BEATTY'S FLATS

miles 10
hours 4½

Magnificent views of all the high peaks in the area can be seen from the great meadows along this trail.

Beatty's Flats, near the site of the original Beatty's Cabin, lies in the heart of the Pecos Wilderness Area, at the junction of the Pecos River and the Rito del Padre (color plate 4, bottom). A focal point of attraction for horseback riders, hikers, and fishermen traveling the Pecos high country, Beatty's can also be reached from Cowles by the Round Mountain trail (Trip 4). The beginnings of Trips 3, 7, and 8 all use Hamilton Mesa Trail.

Trail begins at Iron Gate campground (9,356 ft), at the Pecos Wilderness boundary. Hikers or riders with horse trailers can drive to that point by taking the road that branches from NM-63, at a point 1 mile south of Cowles, for 4.2 miles from the junction. This is an unpaved but graded fair-weather road. From junction, follow this road east up steep hill. At a distance 1.2 miles along this road, at a Forest Service sign, "Grass Mountain Summer Homes Areas," an easy unmarked trail winds southward to the top of Grass Mountain (9,841 ft). The distance by trail from the road to the top is about 2 miles; the climb is approximately 1,100 ft, and the walking time about 1½ hours. The Pennsylvanian sedimentary rocks holding up this mountain are mostly covered by soils, hence the name. The summit of this small, flat-topped mesa is the most accessible high point near Cowles, providing excellent views of some major peaks (photo, p. 70).

From the wide pastures at Geronimo's ranch, 2.6 miles from the beginning of Hamilton Mesa road, is a superb view of Pecos Baldy Peak to the north, as well as west to Santa Fe Baldy and Capulin and Lake Peaks (north and south of Santa

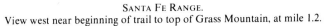

SANTA FE RANGE.
View west near beginning of trail to top of Grass Mountain, at mile 1.2.

RIDERS ON UPPER WESTERN SLOPE OF GRASS MOUNTAIN.
View north across Pecos Canyon to Pecos Baldy (on horizon) and open grassy summit of
Round Mountain. Road to Iron Gate is in valley below.

Fe Baldy, respectively). Photo, p. 39. At a point on road 0.5 mile past Geronimo's, a trail leads to the right, proceeding to the Valle Medio via the deep canyon of Mora River (Trip 9).

Hikers and riders from Cowles can reach Iron Gate campground (about 4 miles) by one of two trails: both start a short distance north of Cowles. Follow the improved road leading north from Cowles general store toward Jacks Creek campground for 0.8 mile. Both trail routes veer off separately to the right just before the improved road crosses Pecos River.

1) For first route, go on secondary road or trail up hill to right, between two houses on broad shoulder above Pecos River, just opposite the mouth of Jacks Creek. Pass through gate, go 50 yards across meadow, and take trail climbing steep hill to right. After about 1 mile, this trail connects with Hamilton Mesa road, 2.5 miles from the junction of this road with NM-63. Turn left, soon passing Geronimo's ranch, and continue along road 1.7 miles to Iron Gate campground. Distance by this route is about 3.5 miles.

2) For second route, descend to right on secondary road to river bottom and cross secondary bridge over Pecos River to northwest side. After passing in front of log house on left, cross bridge over Jacks Creek and continue north along road on west side of Pecos. Road ends on flat in front of log house with rail fence, flanked by massive cliffs of Mississippian limestone on left. Trail climbs hill northward to left of house. At top of hill is an unmarked branch in trail. The left fork turns sharply up steep hill. This trail goes to Jacks Creek campground. Take trail to right, straight ahead, continuing northward, staying well above the Pecos River. Avoid the temptation to take secondary branches of the trail (made by fishermen and campers) that descend to the Pecos River. Along Pecos River irregularly distributed cliffs of dark Precambrian amphibolite disrupt trails near river level. The higher trail stays about 40 to 60 ft above the river for about 1 mile northward, then descends, crossing the Pecos to the east bank by a horse bridge. The trail then ascends gradually up the east side of Pecos valley, through mixed

conifer forests, directly to Iron Gate campground. Distance from Cowles via this trail is about 4 miles. This trail has the advantage over the first route by avoiding travel on Hamilton Mesa road for almost 2 miles.

Distance from Cowles to Beatty's Flats is 10 miles; walking time, about 4½ hours; riding time, 3½ hours. Distance from Iron Gate campground is 6 miles; walking time, about 3 hours; riding time, 2¼ hours. Trail is excellent all the way.

0.0   End of road at Iron Gate campground. Pecos Wilderness Area fence. For the first 2.5 miles, trail goes through mixed conifer and aspen forests. In the first 0.5 mile it climbs southeast via a couple of switchbacks, until it reaches the crest of the mesa, then makes an abrupt sharp turn to the left (northeast) along the narrow crest of the mesa. At that point a secondary trail leads to the right, back along the ridge, southwest to Grass Mountain. Along the crest, Pennsylvanian sandstones dip northwest 8 to 10 degrees. They form southeast-facing cliffs that drop steeply into Rio Mora Canyon. These Pennsylvanian sandstones hold up this high ridge, extending many miles northward. Here, occasional glimpses across the Mora Valley to East (Elk Mountain) Range highlight the scenic grandeur. Trail follows narrow ridge crest northward for about 0.4 mile before beginning a slanting descent along the steep east slope of Hamilton Mesa.

1.1   Signpost at trail intersection. Trail to right leads about 2 miles northeast, angling downward to Mora Flats in bottom of upper Mora Canyon (Trip 8). Take trail straight ahead to Beatty's Flats (also to Pecos Falls). Trail continues through forests along steep east slope of Hamilton Mesa, followed by steady climb northward back onto the crest of the mesa.

2.2   Trail emerges from aspens and rises into great grassy meadows stretching ahead as far as you can see along the top of Hamilton Mesa. Tall blue iris are especially plentiful and lovely in these meadows during moist early summers.

2.8   The first of many magnificent views of Truchas Peaks (color plate 4, top). Far to the north rise the broad crests of Santa Barbara Divide, carved from

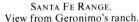

SANTA FE RANGE.
View from Geronimo's ranch.

flat-lying Pennsylvanian sandstone beds. To the northwest towers the rounded summit of Chimayosos Peak, followed southward by the rugged Truchas Peaks, all held up by resistant Precambrian quartzite. Stretching out south of these peaks is the long, low, flat-lying ridge eroded out of almost horizontal Pennsylvanian sandstone and limestone beds, known since the late 19th century as Bordo Lajado by Spanish-American herdsmen who brought their cattle into the high country for summer grazing. Appropriately, this Spanish name means "ridge in rock layers" or "layered ridge." More recently, the steep east face of this ridge has been called Trailrider's Wall. Still farther south rises the huge camelback mass of Pecos Baldy, another lofty summit of Precambrian quartzite. There is also a fine view of the more southerly high West Divide, with its lofty peaks of brown Precambrian granite, seen earlier from Geronimo's.

BLUE IRIS.

4.3   Trail intersection at signpost (10,080 ft). Trail straight ahead along mesa leads to Pecos Falls (Trip 3). Take trail bearing left downslope for Beatty's Flats. This excellent, wide trail, locally rocky with Pennsylvanian sandstone rubble, makes a long, gradual descent through aspen groves and mixed conifer forests.

5.2   Trail junction and signpost, followed by gate. Trail to right (north), after climbing Hamilton Mesa, eventually descends eastward to the Rio Valdez.

On Beatty's trail, just before trail junction, note that boulders of smooth, gray Mississippian limestone abruptly appear on trail. This rock lies close above the contact of Paleozoic sediments with underlying Precambrian rocks, thus marking the near position of the great unconformity. Sure enough, slabby, pearly gray pieces of micaceous Precambrian phyllite soon make their appearance (beyond trail junction and gate).

5.5   Trail descends out of woods into the broad, grassy bottom of Pecos Canyon and crosses wooden bridge. Trail junction at signpost. Trail to left, going southward down the valley, is the alternate Cowles-Beatty's trail via Round Mountain (Trip 4), an interesting return route to Cowles. From the trail junction, you can see great cliffs of white Precambrian quartzite standing high above the river half a mile downstream. Open, flower-rich meadows extend northward along this beautiful valley as far as Beatty's Flats (photo, p. 42).

THREE TRUCHAS PEAKS AND CHIMAYOSOS PEAK (right).
View from Hamilton Mesa.

6.0 Beatty's Flats (here named). At this point, the Rito del Padre enters
Pecos valley from the northwest. The large bluff at the junction of the two
streams is composed of massive, flat-lying pre-Mississippian sandstone beds
resting unconformably on Precambrian micaceous phyllite near river level.
This particular zone of Precambrian rocks is relatively soft compared to the
massive quartzite that crops out a short distance upstream and downstream. Apparently, this zone was once deeply eroded to form a considerable depression in the ancient erosion surface before inundation by a
pre-Mississippian sea. In that same sea was deposited the sandy sediment
now making up the later compacted sandstone beds in this high bluff. The
pre-Mississippian sandstone beds are uncommonly thick at this point,
because of having filled in the erosional depression (photo, p. 42).

Beatty's Flats might well be called the hub of the Pecos Wilderness Area:
it is at the junction of many trails and acts as a focal point to attract riders
and hikers in the upper Pecos region. The best approach to Truchas Lakes
starts here, ascending Rito del Padre (Trip 7). A good trail to Pecos Falls,
4 miles from Beatty's, crosses Rito del Padre northward and climbs the high
east ridge above the Pecos River just beyond.

Some incorrectly assume that the original Beatty's Cabin was located on
Beatty's Flats. Such was not the case. George Beatty, a pioneer prospector,
built his cabin about 1870 on a small flat well above the west side of the
Pecos River, on the north side of the Rito del Padre, opposite the open
meadows here termed Beatty's Flats. Beatty used the little two-room log
cabin with a dirt-covered roof as a base for hunting and prospecting, although the records do not indicate he ever struck it rich! Today, nothing
remains of the cabin but a small overgrown mound of rubble where the
fireplace stood. The Forest Service has mounted a plaque on two posts near

BEATTY'S FLATS.
Site of original Beatty's Cabin is small elevated flat in middle distance, on north side of
Rito del Padre, with bluffs of pre-Mississippian sandstone to left.

the old cabin site. George Beatty, a colorful character with a distinctive goatee, told wild tales of his adventures in the upper Pecos region; and of his close encounters with the many grizzlies that roamed the country. The book *Beatty's Cabin* by Elliott Barker recounts many interesting stories of the Pecos high country.

Two new cabins are located half a mile south of Beatty's Flats, on a grassy slope high above the river, 0.2 mile west of the bridge over the Pecos on Hamilton Mesa trail. These cabins are used as administrative field stations and work sites by the U.S. Forest Service and the New Mexico Department of Game and Fish. They should not be called "Beatty's Cabin."

Trip 3
miles 13
hours 5½

HAMILTON MESA TRAIL—
COWLES TO PECOS FALLS

This trip can be one of the most rewarding of all the trail trips described, for it leads almost to the headwaters of the Pecos River, into a remote and exceptionally beautiful part of the Pecos Wilderness Area. Pecos Falls, cascading over 50 ft, is the only high waterfall in the entire region. The falls are most easily reached by going north along the crest of Hamilton Mesa, after first following Hamilton Mesa-Beatty's trail for 4.3 miles (Trip 2). The trip thence northward along Hamilton Mesa provides spectacular views of Truchas Peaks. In returning to Cowles, we suggest that you take the good trail south along the Pecos River from the falls directly to Beatty's Flats, and then complete the trip via either Round Mountain or Hamilton Mesa trail (Trips 4 and 2).

Distance from Cowles to Pecos Falls is 13 miles; walking time, 5½ hours; riding time, 4 hours. The trails are good, but the trip is long. Leave early if you expect to return to Cowles the same day. See Trip 2 for details of the first 4.3 miles of the trip.

4.3   Trail junction at signpost on Hamilton Mesa. Trail descending to left leads to Beatty's Flats. Follow right fork, straight ahead, to Pecos Falls and Santa Barbara Divide. Trail is in open meadows for next 1.5 miles, but is clearly defined.

5.0   Trail leads along high meadows close below and west of the summit ridge of Hamilton Mesa. A small grove of trees blocks the trail, but the path through them is clear. Trail soon emerges into open meadows again. From here, the round summit knob of the ridge, encircled by flat-lying beds of resistant Pennsylvanian sandstone, is not far upslope to the east.

After you pass this small grove, splendid views of the Truchas Peaks unfold, and the whole mighty amphitheater of canyons and ridges lying below the peaks sharpens into focus. The upper head of the Rito Chimayo-sos drainage, curving northwestward, and expansive meadows along the higher north slopes of the north fork of Rito Azul are especially evident. Far back to the south, the tabletop of Grass Mountain, forming the final southernmost height capping Hamilton Mesa, still can be seen.

5.5   A second spruce-aspen grove climbs the hillside, not far below the west side of the ridge top. More than one trail is here, so stay high up and pass through sparse trees near the upper limits of the grove.

5.7   Trail junction and signpost near top of ridge. Trail to left, which branches just before signpost is reached, goes west, then southwest to intersect Hamilton Mesa to Beatty's trail. Trail to right heads east, down open meadows to Rio Valdez, and eventually joins Rociada trail (Trip 8). Follow track ahead near crest of mesa for Pecos Falls.

6.2   Enter trees at northeast end of meadows. Trail swings over the crest of the divide, to the southeast side, and continues northeast through dense forest of aspen and mixed conifers, either below the crest on the east side or on the crest itself.

7.4   Trail emerges into a large meadow extending downslope eastward to Rio Valdez, as well as upslope to the mesa crest. Several branches of the trail cross the meadows, but all climb the ridge diagonally to the northeast edge of the meadows near summit crest. The views are excellent southeast across the Valdez and Mora Valleys to the East Range. A short walk up to the northwest edge of the meadows provides a striking view of the long Bordo Lajado (layered ridge) between Pecos Baldy and South Truchas Peak. This ridge is held up by flat-lying beds of resistant Pennsylvanian sandstone. At a wooden fence and gate, the trail enters forest of mixed conifers near the summit crest to the northeast. Ahead, the trail climbs along the crest of the ridge a short distance before swinging down on the west side of the mesa, continuing through dense forests. Extensive Pennsylvanian sandstone rubble on trail for the first quarter of a mile.

8.0 Trail enters first of several small meadows after descending rather steeply toward the Pecos River. From here, the broad trail continues north at a more or less constant elevation.

8.8 Trail emerges into open meadows a short distance east of, and still high above, the top of the falls.

Signpost. Trail to right goes over the top of Hamilton Mesa to Rio Valdez and eventually to Gascon trail. Take trail to left, descending rapidly into grassy, willow-rich meadows bordering the Pecos River just above the falls.

9.0 Signpost at Pecos River above falls (10,480 ft). Trail up the Pecos River, to the right, goes north to Santa Barbara Divide and Sky Line trail (3.5 miles). Trail to left leads south to Beatty's Flats (4 miles; walking time, 1½ hours), and makes a good return route to Cowles. Trail is fairly good all the way to Beatty's Flats, staying high above the west bank of the Pecos. It crosses Jarosa Creek amid vast open meadows and beautiful aspen groves, where a second, longer trail to Beatty's branches northwest toward Rito del Padre. The more direct trail, along Pecos valley, finally reaches Beatty's Flats by a winding, fairly steep descent. See Trips 2 or 4 for descriptions of possible routes from Beatty's to Cowles.

An increasing roar of falling water is heard as the falls are approached (100 yards downstream from signpost). After walking through brush, you suddenly emerge at the top of the falls. This spot is beautiful for a picnic lunch—if you have any food left in your saddlebag or knapsack after the long journey!

At the top of the falls you stand on glassy-white Precambrian quartzite, the actual surface marking the unconformable contact between underlying, steeply inclined beds of quartzite, and overlying, almost flat Pennsylvanian shales and sandstones (poorly exposed where the valley side rises above top of falls). Mississippian limestone does not overlie the Precambrian here. The resistant mass of quartzite holding up the falls probably formed an island in the ancient Mississippian sea; thus limestone (deposited in marine water) never could have been deposited here. As the Pennsylvanian seas inundated the area, the same quartzite mass still must have stood well above the irregular, ancient sea floor. Pennsylvanian muds and sands were gradually deposited over this high underwater knob. Modern erosion, in sculpturing the Pecos valley, has cut down through the cover of the relatively soft Pennsylvanian rocks to expose the crest of this extremely tough, underlying quartzite mass. To get by this upward-protruding barrier knob of resistant rock, the present-day river cascades 50 ft vertically over waterfalls and cataracts (color plate 8).

Climbing part way down the cliffs on the west side of the falls, you can see how details of rock structure have controlled the course and attitude of the falls. Quartzite here consists of two main fracture systems (joints).

PECOS FALLS.

East-west joints, running across stream, are the more prominent. These joint surfaces stand almost vertical, because they dip very steeply southward, downstream, at about 70 degrees from horizontal. The falls really consist, therefore, of a series of steps cut out of, and shaped by, the steep, southward-facing surfaces of these joints. But the vertical north-south joints parallel to the course of the stream are the ones that have opened up main lines of weakness across the tilted-up east-west-trending slabs of quartzite athwart the stream, and through which the rushing water has had to break its way. The best photographs of the falls can be taken below them, high on the east bank of the stream.

From the signpost above the falls is a beautiful view northward up broad willow flats and grassy meadows along the Pecos toward the flat-lying summit ridge of the Santa Barbara Divide. All of this gently land-scaped region is an expression of erosion working upon flat-lying sedimentary beds. As mentioned earlier, Santa Barbara Divide and Sky Line trail, about 3.5 miles away, can be reached by going up the Pecos valley. From Santa Barbara Divide, you look northward into the deep valleys of the upper Santa Barbara drainage, all the way to the old Spanish-American town of Peñasco, far to the northwest.

An interesting side trip can be made from Pecos Falls to Lost Bear

D.H. MONEYPENNY.

BEAVER AND BEAVER DAM.

Lake—a small, enchanting, blue-green lake hidden among the trees, perched high on the steep west slope of Hamilton Mesa about 2 miles upstream from the falls. Trail to the lake can be picked up in the brush perhaps 50 yards from the river on the northwest valley side (left side, looking upstream). The trail stays well above marshes and ponds (partly created by beavers) along the river. About a mile and a half north, the valley becomes partly hemmed in on the east by a low, down-sloping ridge extending into the valley from that side, composed of large, jumbled-up blocks of thick-bedded Pennsylvanian sandstone and conglomerate partly overgrown with trees. This ridge probably represents an old landslide. Just before reaching the piled-up blocks of sandstone, you can see rugged cliffs high on the east side of the valley. These cliffs are caused by an isolated knob of resistant Precambrian quartzite projecting upward, surrounded by Pennsylvanian sandstones.

To reach Lost Bear Lake, continue up the main valley another quarter of a mile, as far as the first meadow north of the piled-up sandstone blocks. On reaching a large marker post in this meadow, turn sharply eastward and cross the river. A good blazed trail enters the forest on the east side of the meadow. The lake lies little more than half a mile from here. The trail is excellent, though steep in places. It traverses a thick spruce forest most of the way, climbing several hundred feet. The lake cannot be seen until its actual shore is reached. This spot has unusual charm, especially when the sun shines through the spruce branches into the emerald-green water. No permanent population of fish lives here, as the water is too shallow to prevent winter kill.

Trip 4

ROUND MOUNTAIN TRAIL—
COWLES TO BEATTY'S FLATS

One of two routes from Cowles to Beatty's Flats is by way of Round Mountain trail (see Trip 2 for alternate route via Hamilton Mesa). There is little difference between the two routes; both are excellent trails affording magnificent mountain scenery. The Round Mountain route stays among cool aspen groves and small parklike meadows most of the way. From the high meadows on the south side of Round Mountain, the views of the Santa Fe Range and the Pecos valley are magnificent. These meadows make an excellent short trip (3 miles from Jacks Creek campground). Of special interest is a breathtaking view from the crest of 400-ft-high cliffs down into the gorge of Pecos Canyon 1 mile south of Beatty's Flats (color plate 4, bottom).

The road to Jacks Creek campground goes north from the general store at Cowles, along the east side of Pecos valley, on a road cut into Precambrian amphibolite (diagram, p. 35). After 0.8 mile, a trail and secondary road branch to the right just before the main road curves northwest across the Pecos River. A minor fault, with a displacement of about 100 ft, occurs in this part of the Pecos valley (geology and trail map). The west side of the valley is dropped down in relation to the east side, and the river flows along the fault. After crossing the river to the west side, the road rests on Lower Pennsylvanian sandstones and shales exposed in roadcuts along Jacks Creek Valley at distances of 1.0 and 1.6

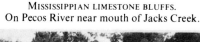

MISSISSIPPIAN LIMESTONE BLUFFS.
On Pecos River near mouth of Jacks Creek.

miles from Cowles. At the second exposure, a thin coal seam can be seen, similar in stratigraphic position to that already observed 10 miles south, on the west side of Pecos valley opposite mile 5.6 on NM-63. The beginning of Jacks Creek campground is reached at a distance of 2.4 miles. Turn right to the lower campground. The trail to Round Mountain begins at the east side of the southern part of the campground. This point is about 2.6 miles by road from Cowles.

Riders and hikers leaving from Cowles who want to avoid traveling all the way to Jacks Creek campground by the road (which has several large switchbacks) may go most of the way by trail, saving about half a mile. To do so, leave the road to the campground 0.8 mile north of Cowles, just before it cross the Pecos River, descend to the right into the river bottom, cross secondary bridge over Pecos River to the northwest side. After passing in front of log house (on left), cross bridge over Jacks Creek and continue north along road on west side of Pecos River. Road ends on flat in front of log house with rail fence; massive Mississippian limestone cliffs on left (photo, p. 47). Trail climbs hill northward to left of house. At top of hill is an unmarked branch in trail: the path straight ahead goes up the Pecos, to Iron Gate campground on Hamilton Mesa. Take the path that turns sharply to the left, ascending the steep hill and swinging westward around the point and up the hill towards Jacks Creek. This trail enters the southwest side of the lower part of Jacks Creek campground. Cross the campground to the base of the hill on the east side, to the signpost at the beginning of the trail. The distance from Cowles by this route is about 2 miles.

From Cowles to Beatty's Flats is about 10 miles; walking time, 4½ hours; riding time, 3½ hours. Distance from Jacks Creek campground, 7.5 miles; walking time, 3½ hours; riding time, 2¾ hours.

0.0 Signpost. East side of southern part of Jacks Creek campground. Trail starts here for Beatty's Flats and also for Pecos Baldy Lake (Trip 5). Trail ascends hillside northeast up long gentle rise, over an excellent wide trail. There are occasional views overlooking Jacks Creek campground, which stretches three-quarters of a mile north-south along the meadows on the east side of Jack's Creek Valley.

1.0 Pecos Wilderness boundary sign. From here on, the trail lies within the Wilderness Area. A short distance north of the sign the trail turns abruptly south in a gentle switchback; then, for the next half a mile, climbs the steep hillside by means of a gentle double switchback through a forest of mixed aspen and conifers. From the beginning, the trail traverses almost flat-lying Lower Pennsylvanian rocks, and in some places, is cut into hillside, exposing thin-bedded layers of shale, siltstone, and limestone. Some beds contain scattered fossils.

1.5 Trail rounds second switchback, turning north abruptly at wooden fence that blocks off old, much steeper trail to the south. Trail climbs forested hillside to the north.

1.9 Trail turns straight across wooded crest of ridge to east side and then veers northward, to east side of crest. Ridge is capped by massive, flat-lying Pennsylvanian sandstone and conglomerate, forming cliffs up to 10 ft high. Locally, considerable sandstone and conglomerate rubble is on the trail.

2.5 Trail makes a broad arc eastward around head of Albright Creek.

2.7 Junction of trail at signpost, shortly after trail emerges into large meadows. Trail to left is to Pecos Baldy Lake (Trip 5) going northwest through aspen groves. For Beatty's Flats, continue straight ahead

PECOS RIVER.
View north towards Beatty's Flats from high cliffs above Pecos Canyon. Santa Barbara Divide on skyline.

(east and then northeast), across meadows. This trail climbs up over the flat top of this southerly meadow-covered ridge of Round Mountain (10,200 ft) and provides excellent views of the Santa Fe Range to the west as well as southward down the Pecos valley. For the next 2 miles the trail skirts the south and east sides of Round Mountain, occasionally passing through clumps of trees, but staying mostly in open meadows.

4.1   Trail enters mixed aspen and conifer forests, passing through scattered small meadows. It turns northeast, gradually dropping in elevation, with the deep gorge of the Pecos River many hundreds of feet below. From the meadows there are excellent views across the valley to Hamilton Mesa on the east.

5.0   Noisy Brook. For the next mile, trail remains almost level and is mostly in aspen groves and occasional meadows. After 1 mile, trail begins to descend rather steeply into Pecos Canyon.

6.3   Watch closely for opening to right of trail, where you can walk out on top of the old erosion surface cut into Precambrian quartzite that forms spectacular, 400-ft-high, almost vertical cliffs along the Pecos Gorge. The layers of quartzite in the cliffs are tilted up very steeply, in striking contrast to the almost flat, unconformably overlying beds of Mississippian and Pennsylvanian sandstones and limestones. Unfortunately, the latter are only poorly exposed in certain places higher upslope. A small but excellent outcrop of the great unconformity (discussion, p. 20) can be seen about 50 yards south along the cliff top, where flat-lying beds of pre-Mississippian sandstone rest directly on the irregular Precambrian quartzite surface (photo, p. 50).

A short distance northward along this same cliff top is an exceptionally

THE "GREAT UNCONFORMITY."
Marked by geological pick.

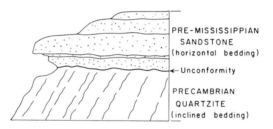

PRE-MISSISSIPPIAN
SANDSTONE
(horizontal bedding)

←Unconformity

PRECAMBRIAN
QUARTZITE
(inclined bedding)

fine vista of the broadening Pecos valley as far north as the open parks around Beatty's Flats. From the cliff top, trail heads almost due west along a small side canyon, in its final descent to the bottom of Pecos valley, a short distance north.

6.5   Trail crosses Beatty's Creek and swings back northeast. Trail junction on north side of creek. Trail to left heads north, staying well above the river. After 0.4 mile it passes two log cabins, administrative cabins of the U.S. Forest Service and the New Mexico Department of Game and Fish. Take trail to right, descending directly to the Pecos River.

6.7   Trail passes through parklike meadows along west side of Pecos, at north end of spectacular canyon cut in Precambrian quartzite. Trail turns northward and traverses beautiful meadows along river.

7.0   To the right is the bridge over the Pecos and Hamilton Mesa trail (Trip 2). Continue straight ahead for Beatty's.

7.5   Beatty's Flats is the name applied to the open parks at the junction of Rito del Padre and the Pecos, opposite the original site of Beatty's Cabin. Several trails radiate from here. Trail up the Padre goes to Truchas Lakes (Trip 7). Trail up the Pecos reaches Pecos Falls (Trip 3). Trail crossing the river at bridge half a mile downstream is Hamilton Mesa trail, an excellent possible return route to Cowles (Trip 2). For a description of the interesting history of Beatty's Cabin and this area, see Trip 2, p. 41-42.

Trip 5

ROUND MOUNTAIN TRAIL— COWLES TO PECOS BALDY LAKE AND SOUTH TRUCHAS PEAK

The most direct route to South Truchas Peak from Cowles is by way of Pecos Baldy Lake.

Pecos Baldy Lake lies in one of the most beautiful settings—as well as in one of the most interesting geological areas—of the Pecos high country. The lake, at an altitude of 11,440 ft lies in a glacial cirque at the foot of the precipitous east face of Pecos Baldy. A great rock dislocation (fault) occurs at this spot, where Pennsylvanian sandstones, shales, and limestones are faulted against Precambrian quartzite of much greater age (cross section diagram, p. 54). A good trail leads from the lake to the top of Pecos Baldy, providing magnificent views of the nearby Truchas Peaks.

Pecos Baldy Lake can be reached from Cowles by either of two routes, Round Mountain trail described here (10 miles), or Dockwiller trail (Trip 6) from Panchuela campground (11 miles). Round Mountain trail is less steep, providing excellent views south and west from high meadows on the south side of that mountain. The second trail could be used as a possible return route to Cowles.

Jacks Creek campground lies 2 miles by trail and 2.5 miles by road north of Cowles (see Trip 4 for description of routes from Cowles to campground).

From Jacks Creek campground to Pecos Baldy Lake is 7.5 miles; walking time, 3½ hours; riding time, 2¾ hours. Walking time from Cowles is 4½ hours; riding time, 3½ hours.

Round Mountain trail starts on the east side of the southernmost part of Jacks Creek campground. For the first 2.7 miles the trail coincides with the Round Mountain route from Cowles to Beatty's Flats (description, Trip 4).

2.7 Trail junction and signpost. Trail straight ahead is to Beatty's (Trip 4). Take trail to left, turning northwest through open aspen groves and small meadows.

3.0 Trail emerges into southwestern part of vast open meadows, turning due north, gradually climbing and skirting upper western slopes of Round Mountain, affording excellent views westward toward Santa Fe Baldy and southward down the Pecos valley below Cowles.

4.5 Trail enters forest of mixed conifers and aspen on northwest side of Round Mountain and descends gradually into Jacks Creek.

5.0 Trail crosses Jacks Creek. Signpost. Trail to west leads back to Cowles via Dockwiller trail, but also with a branch farther on leading westward to Horsethief Meadows. Follow trail northward along Jacks Creek. Trail stays near valley bottom for less than a mile, passing through open parks and aspen groves with numerous wild flowers. The irregular small hills and mounds along the valley here are remnants of outwash material from glaciers once present in the Pecos Baldy area.

5.4 Signpost. Secondary trail to right crosses Jacks Creek and leads to Beatty's Flats via Beatty's Parks. From here on, trail leaves Jacks Creek and gradually ascends north through dense spruce forests to a higher elevation on the valley side. Finally, trail emerges into more open country within half a mile of the lake.

BLUEBELLS.

SHOOTING STAR.

7.5 Signpost and trail junction, just south of Pecos Baldy Lake (11,400 ft).
Sky Line trail crosses at this junction. Left branch climbs steep wooded
ridge to high saddle southwest of Pecos Baldy Lake and continues to
Horsethief Meadows. Trail to right ascends long flat ridge (Bordo Lajado)
stretching northward to Truchas Peaks (Trip 15).

Pecos Baldy Lake nestles at the eastern foot of Pecos Baldy in an am-
phitheaterlike glacial cirque with three steep sides. This cirque, carved
out of solid rock by a large mass of ice that lay here 10,000 to 12,000

BIGHORN SHEEP.

years ago, is dammed up by a low, irregular, piled-up morainal ridge of glacial rock debris which dams the lake on the open southeasterly side of the cirque. The trail junction is located on this moraine, just southeast of the lake. Until the 1930's there was only a small, shallow pond (an acre or two) at the bottom of the large natural cirque; water drained into a cavernous hole in a shattered ledge of limestone at the bottom of the basin. "One could climb down into it for thirty feet or more" (Elliott Barker, in *Beatty's Cabin*). The New Mexico Department of Game and Fish plugged the hole and began the development of a larger lake suitable for trout. Some years later, the U.S. Forest Service constructed a small dam, raising the lake level a few additional feet. Today, Pecos Baldy Lake is the largest and one of the most beautiful high mountain lakes in the Pecos Wilderness. It has no normal outlet, but the water has a subterranean outflow, seeping between the coarse glacial boulders and coming to the surface again near Jacks Creek.

Bighorn sheep were introduced into the Pecos Wilderness in the early 1960's. These majestic animals have thrived, particularly in the Pecos Baldy area, and can often be seen in the saddle northeast of Pecos Baldy Lake and on the slopes of Pecos Baldy.

Immediately beyond the lake rises the great mass of Pecos Baldy, composed of gray-white Precambrian quartzite. The southwest branch of Sky Line trail (Trip 15), starting at the trail junction southeast of the lake, goes up the heavily wooded ridge on the southwest side of the lake. This trail first comes out into the open southwest of the lake on a high saddle underlain by gray shale. An easy hiking trail climbs from this point to the east summit of Pecos Baldy (12,529 ft). To the west, a sharp ridge lies between this higher summit and the west peak, rising to 12,500 ft. From these summits are magnificent views in all directions, particularly north to the

BIGHORN SHEEP.
Saddle north of Pecos Baldy Lake.

WEST SUMMIT OF PECOS BALDY.
Santa Fe Range on far horizon.

nearby Truchas Peaks, west to the Jemez Mountains across the wide Rio Grande valley, and south over the lower Pecos valley to Glorieta Mesa in the far distance.

A great north-south fault passes between the western edge of Pecos Baldy Lake and the precipitous northeastern face of Pecos Baldy. The fault plane is nearly vertical, separating Precambrian quartzite that forms the entire peak, from bedded Middle Pennsylvanian limestones, shales, and sandstones on the east and southeast. Pennsylvanian gray shales on the high saddle southwest of the lake (already mentioned), are located against the fault. A fine but partial sequence of Pennsylvanian rocks is exposed on the saddle and on the high Bordo Lajado directly north of the lake. The rocks, steeply dipping in the saddle near the fault, flatten out away from the fault toward the east. The fault curves northwest from the saddle north of Pecos Baldy Lake, around the head of the middle fork of the Rio Medio drainage, then veers northeast to recross the divide near the foot of the south shoulder of South Truchas Peak.

BRYOZOAN.
Fenestrellina.

CORAL.
Lophophyllidium.

Middle Pennsylvanian fossils, particularly brachiopods, corals, and bryozoans, are common in several sedimentary layers exposed in the saddle. Small horn corals, averaging 1 to 1½ inches in length, that lived on an ancient sea bottom, occur abundantly in, and weather out of, the gray shales and thin limestones cropping out in the lowest part of the saddle. In general appearance, these fossil corals are not unlike some modern marine corals, though differing in structural details.

A rather obscure secondary trail, very poor for horses, can be picked up some distance down the steep slope north and northwest below the saddle (north of Pecos Baldy Lake) and used, if needed, to eventually reach the trail descending westward down the Rio Medio.

The easiest and most direct route from Cowles to South Truchas Peak is by way of Pecos Baldy Lake. Experienced climbers can readily climb South Truchas Peak from a camp at Pecos Baldy Lake (4 miles) and return the same day. Follow the Sky Line trail north from the trail junction near the lake, along the crest of Bordo Lajado. See Trip 15 for detailed description.

PECOS BALDY LAKE.

CROSS SECTION THROUGH RIDGE NORTH OF PECOS BALDY LAKE.

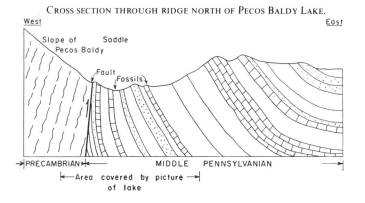

Trip 6

miles 10
hours 4½

DOCKWILLER TRAIL AND
MYSTERY RIDGE–COWLES TO
PECOS BALDY LAKE

One of the two routes from Cowles to Pecos Baldy Lake is the Dockwiller trail over Mystery Ridge, the lofty, precipitous divide between Panchuela and Jacks Creeks. This trail starts from the Panchuela campground. The alternate route (Trip 5), via Round Mountain, starts from Jacks Creek campground. The choice between the two routes depends primarily on which departure point is more convenient. Dockwiller trail is the steeper of the two and about 1 mile longer. It remains in forest most of the way to Jacks Creek, passing through some grand aspen groves and cool glades opening within evergreen forests. From Jacks Creek onward, the two routes follow the same trail to Pecos Baldy Lake.

Panchuela campground (8,360 ft) is 1.5 miles by road north of Cowles (see Trip 1 for road description).

From Panchuela campground to Pecos Baldy Lake is 8.5 miles; walking time is 4 hours; riding time, 3 hours. Walking time from Cowles is 4½ hours; riding time, 3½ hours.

0.0   North end of Panchuela campground, where trail crosses small bridge to east side of Panchuela Creek and heads north. Flat Early Pennsylvanian beds of dark shale and limestone can be seen in bluff above bridge. Fossils, mostly brachiopods and crinoid fragments, can be collected here, especially in some of the thin, limy shale strata weathered to brown.

     For riders and hikers coming from Cowles, passing through the Panchuela campground is not necessary. On the hillside opposite the gate to Panchuela Ranger Station, on road 1.3 miles north of Cowles, is a signpost on a trail that stays above the campground, on west side of valley and joins the trail 0.3 mile north of campground.

0.3   Unmarked trail junction. Trail from southwest (from ranger station) crosses Panchuela Creek and joins trail, in open meadow. Trail continues northwest on northeast side of creek.

0.8   Trail junction and signpost at Pecos Wilderness boundary sign. Trail straight ahead to Cave Creek and Horsethief Meadows. Take Dockwiller trail to right, beginning ascent up steep side of Mystery Ridge prominence, forming the high drainage divide between Pancheula and Jacks Creeks. For the next mile, the trail climbs almost 800 ft through dense forest by a

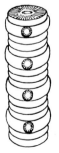

× 1/10

BRACHIOPOD.
Sandia.

CRINOID.
Left, stem fragment; right, restoration of a crinoid.

BLUE IRIS AND YELLOW LUPINE.

series of rather steep switchbacks. The strata are poorly exposed, but blocks of Pennsylvanian sandstone are seen on the trail.

1.8   Trail crosses crest of ridge to east side, turning northward. For the next several miles, the trail generally stays high on the wooded east side of Mystery Ridge. The angle of climb northward is moderate, and the trail passes alternately through beautiful great aspen groves, with some unusually large trees, and more shaded spruce and fir forests. From here on, the trail is easy. Abundant seasonal wild flowers, including blue iris, grow in many of the meadows.

4.9   Trail junction and signpost, in small meadow. Trail to left (northwest) to Horsethief Meadows or Pecos Baldy Lake via Rito Perro (Trip 15). Take trail to right. Trail passes over several irregular, hummocky, and extremely rocky ridges, chiefly composed of loose blocks of Pennsylvanian sandstone. These ridges represent outwash material from glaciers once present in the Pecos Baldy area, located two miles north.

6.0   Trail junction and signpost, just northwest of Jacks Creek. Trail to right leads to Round Mountain and eventually to Jacks Creek campground. Take trail to left, up Jacks Creek. Pecos Baldy Lake lies 2.5 miles away. For a description, see Trip 5, beginning at mile 5.0.

Trip 7

miles 7
hours 4½

BEATTY'S FLATS TO TRUCHAS LAKES
AND THE TRUCHAS PEAKS

Beatty's Flats, 10 miles from Cowles via either Hamilton Mesa or Round Mountain trails, is the starting point for a number of trails leading toward Truchas Lakes and Truchas Peaks. For high mountain grandeur, these trails are undoubtedly among the finest in the upper Pecos region.

Although the most direct route to Truchas Lakes follows the north fork of Rito Azul, the trail crosses extensive bogs that can be extremely bad, and at certain times of the year are impassable for horses. A second, somewhat longer trail in the same region has comparatively minor bogs. The upper drainages of both the Azul and Chimayosos streams have scattered boggy patches making it impossible to find any dry routes across these areas. Probably the best route for horses is a longer, more circuitous one (not described here in detail), almost due north up the Rito del Padre to the southeast slope of Chimayosos Peak, then west on the Sky Line trail along the foot of North Truchas to the lakes. This is a particularly scenic route; some of the most spectacular views of Truchas Peaks are from the south slope of Chimayosos Peak. From Beatty's Flats to the Lakes by this trail is about 8.5 miles.

From Beatty's to Truchas Lakes via the north fork of Rito Azul is about 7 miles. Walking time from Beatty's is 4 to 5 hours; riding time, 3½ to 4 hours.

Signs and map distances inadequately represent mileages actually covered and do not fully allow for winding trails. An important factor to consider—especially for hikers—is altitude. Beatty's lies at 9,400 ft; the Truchas Lakes are at 11,900 ft, and South Truchas Peak rises to 13,100 ft.

0.0 Beatty's Flats. Trail follows northward along west bank of Rito del Padre. The contact between overlying early Mississippian beds and underlying Precambrian rocks here is at about the level of the creek. Small cliffs on both sides of the creek are early or pre-Mississippian sandstone resting directly on the Precambrian contact surface; the sandstone occurs beneath beds of undoubted Mississippian limestone. As trail climbs higher to the north, this contact surface would normally tend to angle still lower beneath a level surface. But a hill of hard Precambrian quartzite rising hundreds of feet above this ancient erosion surface (the great unconformity, p. 20) a short distance north soon elevates the surface high above creek level.

Near Beatty's Flats the Precambrian rocks consist mostly of relatively soft micaceous phyllites. Presumably, these phyllites were deeply eroded into low areas on the ancient erosion surface before the Mississippian seas—in which thick sandy and limy sediments were deposited—flooded that surface.

0.2 Cliff on west side of Padre has flat-lying pre-Mississippian sandstone resting on almost vertical beds of Precambrian quartzite, about 40 ft above trail. Here the hill of resistant quartzite begins to rise rapidly, lifting the great unconformity high above the level of trail and creek.

0.6 Cliffs of Precambrian quartzite along west side of valley. Trail crosses to east bank via horse bridge. Cliffs above trail on right are white Precambrian quartzite interlayered with thin beds of mica schist and fine-grained micaceous phyllite. Certain schist beds contain poorly formed twin

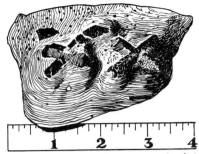

STAUROLITE TWIN CRYSTALS IN MICA SCHIST (*scale in inches*).

crystals of staurolite, a brown aluminum silicate mineral of metamorphic origin.

1.1   Trail crosses to northwest bank of Rito del Padre just above its intersection with Rito de los Chimayosos. Within a short distance, signpost and trail intersection are reached. Trail to right up the Padre (good for horses) climbs north until it eventually reaches Santa Barbara Divide at the southeast slope of Chimayosos Peak, where it intersects Sky Line trail; a good route to Truchas Lakes. The most direct trail for Truchas Lakes turns left, climbing over high knob of Precambrian quartzite at end of ridge between the Padre and Chimayosos. Cresting the ridge, the trail crosses the great unconformity, indicated by Mississippian limestone rubble on the trail. Farther on, the rubble changes to Pennsylvanian sandstone as the trail rises in the stratigraphic section. Ridge here consists mostly of broad grassy slopes. Sharp peak of South Truchas can be seen far ahead to the northwest.

Rumors still persist, particularly in the Rio Grande valley west of the Sangre de Cristo, that the lost Padre mine, said to have been once a rich source of gold, is somewhere in this general area. Long ago, according to legend, the mine was worked by people conscripted from the Rio Grande valley by a padre in Chimayo—hence the name Chimayosos (people of Chimayo), for both the creek and the peak near its head to the north. Some think this mine may lie hidden beneath a rock slide.

In *Beatty's Cabin*, Elliott Barker describes another legend, alternate to the gold mine theory, for the origin of the name Rito del Padre. He reports that priests, particularly from the east side of the mountains—possibly from the Pecos area—may have come into the high country in the late 19th century to hold outdoor mass during the summer months for the numerous Spanish-American sheep herders who worked here. Reportedly, the most common spot for such ceremonies was a grassy bench above what is now called the Rito del Padre, about a mile above its junction with Rito de los Chimayosos.

1.9   Soon after trail drops down to level of Rito Chimayosos, the intersection with the Rito Azul, flowing in from the west, is reached. In the creek bank opposite mouth of Azul are outcrops of almost flat-lying Pennsylvanian sandstone beds. Post, but no sign, on east side of Chimayosos, near mouth of Azul; an obvious trail heads north on east side of the Chimayosos. Cross Chimayosos to west side just above mouth of Azul, to a second post. Pick up trail here. Climb steeply to west, well above the Azul on the north side, through forest of mixed aspen and conifers and a few small meadows.

2.3   Post, but no sign, marks junction of trail at southeast edge of great meadows, at least 120 ft above the Azul. Left trail heads west up the Azul, eventually bearing southwest up the south fork of the Azul. That trail could be taken to reach the foot of Bordo Lajado, and on to Pecos Baldy Lake. For Truchas Lakes, take trail to the right and northwest, skirting upper edge of high grassy meadows and staying well above the main branch of Rito Azul. This trail continues northwest over a mile and a half, hugging the upper edges of the great meadows, but here and there passing through conifer and aspen forests. This trail continually climbs, but is not steep, and remains distinct and easy to follow in all places. Wildflowers are numerous in the meadows. Good views of Bordo Lajado are frequent; it is a ridge of rock layers composed of flat-lying Pennsylvanian strata.

3.9   Major trail junction and signpost (11,080 ft), in large high meadow on the broad divide between Rito Azul and the Chimayosos drainage to the northeast. Three additional trails branch from this junction.

Trail to the left, a secondary trail to Pecos Baldy Lake, goes southwest, then south along the base of the Bordo Lajado to Pecos Baldy Lake.

Trail straight ahead is the old and most direct route to Truchas Lakes, but this trail should not be taken by horses because of bad bogs stretching more than half a mile along part of the trail, making travel for horses extremely difficult even in dry seasons. Distance to the lakes on this trail is about 2.3 miles from this junction. The first 1.4 miles climbs gradually through conifer forests, cutting northward across the various upper drainages of the Chimayosos. The next 0.5 mile goes through the very boggy meadows already mentioned. Just past these boggy meadows, the trail joins

SOUTH TRUCHAS PEAK.
From near head of the Rito Azul. Main peak in background.

SOUTH, MIDDLE AND NORTH TRUCHAS PEAKS.
View from southwest slope of Chimayosos Peak.

Sky Line trail, coming in from the left (south). Final 0.4 mile ascent climbs steeply northwestward to Truchas Lakes, passing through a series of open meadows with partial views of South and Middle Truchas Peaks. Just before this final ascent is an opportunity to observe attractive and rare minerals, and the occurrence of many interesting mica schists and dark, hornblende-rich amphibolite gneisses. Black tourmaline prisms occur in some schists, and the rare, pink manganese-bearing mineral, piedmontite (related to commoner yellow-green epidote) can be found associated with an odd, pinkish, manganiferous mica. These rocks belong to an eastward extension of the wide schist zone crossing between Middle and South Truchas Peaks (geology and trail map).

The Forest Service has opened a new trail from this major junction (at 3.9 miles) to the Truchas Lakes, to bypass the bad bogs on the old trail. Truchas Lakes are about one mile farther on this trail; about 3.4 miles from the junction. Of the two trails, the new one is certainly safer for horses, despite some bogs. Hikers should consider taking this trail, either to or from the lakes, because it provides spectacular views of the Truchas Peaks from the southwest slopes of Chimayosos Peak—as fine as any view in the upper Pecos area. This new trail cuts across several middle-to-upper branches of Rito de los Chimayosos and heads for the saddle between North Truchas and Chimayosos Peaks. A description of this trail follows:

Take trail to right from junction (at 3.9 miles). First part of trail, through conifer forests, crosses level divide immediately and drops steadily.

5.5   After proceeding about a mile and a half, first through a small boggy area, then crossing several small creeks and making broad loops south,

EAST SUMMIT OF MIDDLE TRUCHAS PEAK.

then north (to avoid difficulties of the terrain), trail reaches branching forks of small stream. After crossing first branch, the trail continues north between the two branches. Almost flat beds of Pennsylvanian conglomerate are exposed here, not far above Mississippian limestone (the rubble farther back on the trail).

5.8   After passing through some beautiful small meadows where countless red primroses bloom from early to mid-summer, trail emerges from trees into larger meadows ascending toward base of saddle between Chimayosos and North Truchas Peaks. Precambrian quartzite rock talus has fallen coming downslope from nearby Chimayosos Peak. This rubble conceals the great fault that can be seen farther to the south, cutting the saddle at the east edge of Pecos Baldy, just north of Pecos Baldy Lake (diagram and photo, p. 55, and geology and trail map). This major fault separates Precambrian quartzite on the west and northwest from Pennsylvanian sedimentary rocks to the southeast. Younger rocks to the southeast have been down-dropped hundreds of feet by movement along this fault.

6.2   Signpost and trail junction with Sky Line trail (Trip 15) near base of southwest slope of Chimayosos Peak. Sky Line trail, to right, leads to Santa Barbara Divide; to left, to Truchas Lakes. From the grassy slopes near this junction are magnificent views of the Truchas Peaks (color photos, photo gallery)—the only vantage point in the upper Pecos region where all three lofty summits can be seen at close range. The entire trip is worthwhile for this view alone.

Trail to Truchas Lakes proceeds west near the base of North Truchas Peak, crossing boulder fields of white quartzite rubble that are partly timbered in the lower areas and covered elsewhere with beautiful meadows and wild flowers. The trail is rocky but good, and provides continuously interesting views of the peaks.

7.3   Truchas Lakes (11,900 ft). At the lakes is an awe-inspiring view of the three Truchas Peaks, whose mighty walls of Precambrian quartzite tower over 1,000 ft directly above. The lower lake has been deepened by a dam and is kept stocked with trout. The upper lake is smaller and contains no fish. Few trees grow at this altitude, but flowers and small alpine meadows are lush and beautiful. During late June and July, masses of red primroses cover the meadows.

MIDDLE TRUCHAS PEAK.
Mighty cliffs tower above lowermost of Truchas Lakes.

RED PRIMROSE.

Middle Truchas Peak (13,066 ft) can be climbed from the lakes by ascending the very steep, partly grassy slope to the saddle just northeast of the Peak. South Truchas Peak (13,100 ft) is best climbed from farther south—from the north end of Bordo Lajado. To reach that point, go south along the base of South Truchas, following Sky Line trail (Trip 15) for about 3 miles.

Trip 8

miles 12
hours 6½

COWLES TO MORA FLATS, AND
TRAILS TO EAST DIVIDE

Initially, the trail to Mora Flats and the East Divide crosses Hamilton Mesa eastward into the wilder, middle part of the deeply cut Rio Mora Canyon. Then it climbs the high East Divide, where spectacular views unfold: to the east, the plains country beyond the beautiful Rociada Valley; to the west, the high peaks of the upper Pecos region. Some refer to this trail as the "Edge of the World" because of a spectacular drop in elevation eastward from the East Divide and a seemingly limitless view over the High Plains.

Although nearly inaccessible, the upper Rio Mora is considered by many to be one of the best fishing streams in the southern Sangre de Cristo Range.

Trail starts from Iron Gate campground, about 4 miles northeast of Cowles (see Trip 2 for information on trails from Cowles to Iron Gate). From the campground to Mora Flats is about 3 miles; walking time, 1½ hours; riding time, 1¼ hours.

Two trails reach the East Divide from Mora Flats. The best known is Rociada trail from the north end of the flats up the Rito del Oso. The Rociada is a particularly steep, exceptionally rocky trail with few switchbacks. It emerges onto the East Divide in a vast, broad meadow (an old burned area), affording spectacular views. From Mora Flats (9,200 ft) to the East Divide (11,300 ft) is about 5 miles; walking time, 3 to 4 hours; riding time 2 to 2½ hours.

A much better trail, also about 5 miles long, ascends the East Divide from the southern end of Mora Flats, going up the ridge north of Rito de los Esteros. A good trail (not too rocky) with several appropriate and well-engineered switchbacks, it reaches the East Divide about 2 miles south of the Rociada cattle crossing; but the best distant views are not here. Both trails can be used for an

STEEP CANYON OF THE UPPER RIO MORA.
View north from west slope of East Divide.

interesting loop trip, perhaps ascending by the steeper Rito del Oso trail, which reaches the ridge-top meadow and vantage point for a fine view, and returning on the same day to Mora Flats by the Rito de los Esteros route.

The route from Iron Gate to Mora Flats follows the regular Hamilton Mesa trail for the first 1.1 miles (see Trip 2 for description of this part of route).

1.1   Trail junction and signpost. Trail to left is Hamilton Mesa trail to Beatty's Flats and Pecos Falls. Take trail to right, angling northeast down the east side of Hamilton Mesa through beautiful aspen and spruce groves. Farther down, you can catch occasional glimpses of the deep Mora Canyon far below. As with other trails on Hamilton Mesa, occasional poor exposures of almost flat-lying beds of Pennsylvanian sandstones and shales occur.

1.5   With little drop in elevation, trail continues northward along poorly exposed, flat-lying Mississippian limestone, a short distance upslope from granite cliffs.

2.5   Trail descends across the great unconformity (p. 20) onto cliff tops of tan to pink Precambrian granite, weathered into irregular, rounded masses. As trail descends from here, you look down on Mora Flats (Vega Mora), a series of partly open, grassy river flats developed on the surface of river-deposited gravels, sands, and muds. These flats extend along the Rio Mora about 2 miles.

3.0   Trail junction at west margin of Mora Flats, at base of Hamilton Mesa (9,200 ft). Trail to north leads up Rio Valdez, first following a narrow canyon cut into tough granite for about one mile, then into a more and more open grassy valley where the great unconformity, together with its overlying Paleozoic sediments, descends to creek level. This is a good horseback trail to Beatty's Flats after crossing Hamilton Mesa. It also connects with Gascon trail (Trip 3, p. 44) and eventually, Sky Line trail on Santa Barbara Divide (Trip 15) by proceeding far north toward the head of Rio Valdez. Take trail to east and cross Mora River.

3.1   Unmarked trail intersection in middle of Mora Flats. Trail to right goes downstream, across boggy areas on the flats, then climbs eastward from Mora Canyon up the excellent trail on the north side of Rito de los Esteros (Creek of the Marshes) Canyon, an eastern tributary of Mora River. It reaches the East Divide (5 miles) at a point on Sky Line trail about half a mile north of Spring Mountain and 2 miles south of where Rociada trail reaches the East Divide.

The lower end of Mora Flats passes southward into a deep, narrow gorge cut in tan granite. This steep gorge begins opposite the mouth of Rito de los Esteros, extending a full 6 miles south almost to the junction of the Mora and Pecos Rivers. Tough, tan granite continues for much of this distance, almost to the mouth of Bear Creek, followed in turn by massive, gray-black amphibolite the remaining distance to the Pecos River. There is no trail down most of this lower part of Mora Canyon.

For the Rociada trail ascending Rito del Oso, turn left and follow north along the grassy meadows in the northern part of Mora Flats.

3.8   Trail crosses the Mora to north side and heads eastward up the canyon bottom. Brown granite cliffs are seen repeatedly, close above trail. Note that most of the boulders in the Mora River bed are composed not of this surrounding granite, but of the more resistant Precambrian quartzite brought down from the great quartzite cliffs in upper Mora Canyon.

GEOLOGISTS' CAMP IN HIGH COUNTRY.
Note rock specimens on log.

4.4   Trail junction on northwest bank of Mora. Trail to left continues up Mora Valley for 0.7 mile, then climbs steeply northward out of the canyon onto the high divide between the Mora and Valdez Rivers, known as Bordo del Medio (Middle Ridge). This trail eventually joins Gascon trail east of Pecos Falls. Continuing on foot up the main Mora Valley past the point where Bordo del Medio trail climbs out of the canyon is possible, though extremely difficult. Along this part of the Mora, there is no clear trail; about one mile past the Rociada trail crossing, the valley narrows into a series of box canyons interspersed with more open valley sections containing broad meadows. The beginning of these box canyons coincides with a change from hard Precambrian granite to even harder, glassy-white Precambrian quartzite, forming vertical cliffs rising hundreds of feet above the river. The broader, meadow-rich areas between the quartzite "boxes" are cut from less resistant Precambrian mica schist. Some of this glistening schist, several miles north near the head of the main canyon, is extraordinarily rich in brown staurolite crystals as much as 3 inches long. North of that point, the contact with overlying Mississippian sediments is reached. There, where the canyon flattens out close to its head, it is crossed by the good east-west trail leading from Gascon, north of Rociada, to the upper Valdez and Pecos Canyons, one of the entrance-ways to the Pecos Wilderness.

    Here Rociada trail crosses to the southeast bank of the Mora, just below the mouth of the Rito del Oso, and continues generally eastward, crossing the Oso several times as it climbs steeply out of the deep Mora Valley. This trail, in contrast to most other mountain trails, is broad and often consists of several braided, closely paralleling tracks that continually branch, then converge, going straight up the steep, rocky hillsides. Early each summer, Spanish-Americans from Rociada Valley in the foothills east of the mountains bring large numbers of cattle into the region of the upper Pecos via

MULE DEER.

this trail. The cattle are allowed to graze specified areas of the upper Pecos region in accordance with grazing permits from the U.S. Forest Service. Most of these cattle graze for the entire summer in the great meadows on Hamilton Mesa and elsewhere, and are then driven back across the mountains to Rociada before the fall snows.

Rito del Oso (Creek of the Bear) received its name after a naturalist, Professor L. L. Dyche, first visited the upper Pecos region in the summers of 1881 and 1882. He came from the Rociada country, across the East Divide, along a route that was probably similar to the latter part of this trip. Although he came to collect museum specimens of deer, elk, and other mammals, he was particularly interested in seeking out the large grizzly bear. He established his "bear trail" camp on this creek (which thus became known as the Rito del Oso), somewhere near the present-day trail. Dyche saw numerous large grizzlies in the immediate area, and his diary records many exciting adventures in the wilds of the high country in the early 1880's. For a colorful account of these adventures, see Elliott Barker's book, *Beatty's Cabin*. The latter part of this trip, from Sapello Canyon into the upper Pecos region, is vividly described in the early pages of the book, and was the general route followed by Barker as a boy in the early 1900's.

7.1   After 2.5 miles of following the winding, steep, rocky valley of the Rito

GRIZZLY BEAR.

ROCIADA VALLEY AND THE PLAINS BEYOND.
View from the summit of the East Divide.

del Oso, the trail turns eastward, heads straight upslope, and passes from an open conifer forest into an old burned area now marked by second growth of small fir and spruce. The change from boulders of tan to pink granite, to boulders of massive, grayish Pennsylvanian sandstone is fairly abrupt. The trail has now climbed high enough to reach the level of the sedimentary beds that are the stratigraphic equivalent of those capping Hamilton Mesa. Mississippian limestone is present here, but is mainly covered by blocks of Pennsylvanian sandstone that have rolled downhill from higher up. Discontinuous outcrops of Mississippian limestone, forming small cliffs, can be found about half a mile north of the trail at this point. In these cliffs, the limestone is somewhat thinner than is typical in the Pecos valley and contains abundant quartz grains and pebbles of Precambrian quartzite. These were originally derived from surface weathering of islands of that rock high above Mississippian seas a short distance north (p. 16). From here on, the countryside becomes more open, and the trail less steep, as the crest of the East Divide is approached.

8.0 Crest of East Divide (11,300 ft). On clear days, you can see almost 100 miles eastward across the vast expanse of the High Plains. Southeastward, the granite mass of Hermit's Peak, slightly northwest of Las Vegas, is visible. You can also look almost 2,000 ft straight down into Sapello Canyon and other adjacent, equally deep canyons cut into the steep east face of the Sangre de Cristo Mountains. Here also are magnificent views to the west, of the entire upper Pecos high country.

The trail leading on to Rociada, marked "Sparks Trail," descends a very steep, rocky ridge eastward, dropping nearly 3,000 ft in slightly more than 2 miles. Sky Line trail proceeds north and south from here, along the crest of the East Divide, which is heavily timbered for the most part: About 6 miles north, the Sky Line trail connects with Gascon trail. Two miles south, it intersects the good trail branching westward down Rito de los Esteros, to return to Mora Flats. Another 5.5 miles farther south, it reaches the jeep road from Pecos valley, near Elk Mountain (Trip 10).

Trip 9

COWLES TO LOWER MORA CANYON AND THE VALLE MEDIO

On this trip, you will descend into the deep gorge of lower Mora River, and after reaching Valle Medio beyond, enjoy beautiful views of lower Pecos valley and the high mountains of the West (Santa Fe) Divide. This is a favorite short riding trip from Cowles and is also frequently used by fishermen. The Spanish name, Valle Medio (Middle Valley), designates the extensive meadows high atop the ridge between Bear Creek and Rito de las Trampas (Creek of the Traps), two eastern tributary creeks of the lower Rio Mora, due east of Grass Mountain and Cowles.

From Cowles to lower Mora Canyon is 4 miles; riding time, 1½ hours; walking time, 2 hours. The trail follows Hamilton Mesa trail for the first 2.2 miles from Cowles and takes off from Hamilton Mesa road 3.0 miles from its junction with Highway 63. See Trip 2 for details of this part of the trip.

From lower Mora Canyon to Valle Medio is 3 miles; riding time, 1¼ hours; walking time, 1½ hours; to the far east end of the meadows, about 5.5 miles.

2.2 Sign post to right of road, half a mile past Geronimo's ranch, marks the start of trail heading east over Hamilton Mesa ridge for Valle Medio. Road straight ahead leads to Iron Gate campground and the beginning of Hamilton Mesa trail. Trail climbs gently eastward between two fences through aspen groves. After proceeding about half a mile uphill, fence corner on right marks where a secondary trail ascends southward (less than a mile) to the top of Grass Mountain (9,841 ft). Various other trails go to Grass Mountain from Cowles (Trip 2).

2.9 Trail climbs over narrow wooded crest of Hamilton Mesa ridge (9,400 ft), then descends steep slope, dropping eastward to the bottom of lower Mora Canyon, 700 ft below. Occasional poor exposures of early Pennsylvanian sandstones and shales occur near the top of the ridge. At a point some 400 ft above the river, trail is far enough down vertically to reach the thin, poorly exposed layers of dense, light-gray Mississippian limestone lying close above the Precambrian. Trail soon drops abruptly below the great unconformity (p. 20) to reach the more continuous rocky exposures of tan Precambrian granite forming the precipitous cliffs along much of the gorge of the lower Mora. The trail descends through the granite cliffs in a series of steep switchbacks.

4.0 Trail crosses the Rio Mora (8,730 ft). The river here is a rushing mountain torrent with little pools, many riffles, and small falls—a much-favored fishing area, well worth the trip over Hamilton Mesa from Cowles.

There are no easily accessible trails following this part of the narrow, steep-sided canyon. Trail to Valle Medio climbs steeply eastward out of the gorge through conifers and aspen. After climbing about 500 ft, trail once again crosses the great unconformity by passing upward out of the tan granite, across overlying Mississippian limestone rubble. From here on, few rock exposures, and rarely, loose blocks of Pennsylvanian sandstone, are seen.

5.4 Trail junction and signpost in partly open aspen grove. Trail to left leads

SANTA FE RANGE.
From the top of Grass Mountain. Santa Fe Baldy on left. Much the same view may be seen from the Valle Medio.

upslope and emerges after about a mile in fine, large meadows, the Valle Largo. Trail to right also goes upslope 0.7 mile, as far as the smaller meadows below the main Valle Largo. Trail is poorly marked in this area: avoid heading off eastward on game and cattle trails into the lowest meadows of Valle Largo. Trail to Valle Medio turns south abruptly, crossing the upper part of a small tributary valley entering the Mora about half a mile downstream from the trail crossing. In places, trail is poorly marked as it passes southward through scattered meadows and groves of aspen and spruce.

7.0   Trail suddenly emerges at western end of the great meadows of Valle Medio that extend continuously for over 2 miles east along high bluffs on the north side of Bear Creek. These are among the most luxuriant of all the high mountain meadows of upper Pecos country, with bunchgrass 3 ft high and an abundance of wild flowers throughout the summer. Deer and elk are seen frequently. A walk east to the higher meadows affords magnifi-

ELK.

cent views down the Pecos valley. A walk westward provides views over the top of Grass Mountain to Santa Fe Baldy and Lake Peak. Various trails extend eastward through the meadows, which reach elevations over 10,500 ft.

9.5   Trail junction and signpost (10,560 ft) in the trees at the high northeast-ernmost end of Valle Medio. Good trail, bearing right, leads 4 miles north-east along a wooded ridge to crest of East Divide, where the Sky Line trail is intersected (Trip 15). Second trail, straight ahead, proceeds northward around the headwaters of Rito de las Trampas to Mora Flats (4 miles). Another trail, turning sharply left to the southwest, then west, crosses the beautiful, large meadows of Valle Largo. This latter trail provides a pleas-ant, shorter return route to Mora River and Cowles, a distance of about 3.5 miles to the Mora River.

Trip 10

miles 10.2
hours 2

MICA MINE JEEP ROAD—
MOUTH OF
WILLOW CREEK TO EAST
(ELK MOUNTAIN) DIVIDE

The mouth of Willow Creek, a small eastern tributary of the Pecos River north of Terrero, lies 15.6 miles north of Pecos and 4.1 miles south of Cowles. This is the site of the dumps of the abandoned Pecos mine, formerly one of the great zinc-lead-copper mines of the Southwest. A rough, poorly maintained secondary road starts here, ascending the south fork of Willow Creek to the East Divide at a point slightly north of Elk Mountain. The divide is 11,400 ft, compared to 7,800 ft where the road begins near Willow Creek. From the mouth of Willow Creek to the East Divide is 10.2 miles. From the divide, sweeping views of the country extend far out onto the eastern plains.

This road, built during World War II to stimulate the production of strategic mica from a mine 2 miles east of the divide, is a fair jeep road in dry weather, but is too steep and rocky for passenger cars. In wet weather the road is virtually impassable and can be slippery and extremely dangerous.

0.0   Road starts at the dumps of the old Pecos mine. For 2 miles it winds back and forth across Willow Creek. The contact between underlying Precambrian rocks, here dark amphibolite and pink granite, and the overlying flat beds of Mississippian and Pennsylvanian sediments is only 50 ft above the canyon bottom where the road begins. Because this contact surface is tilted up toward the east at about 10 degrees and the road initially climbs east up the canyon on a grade much less than 10 degrees, the contact climbs higher and higher above the canyon bottom for the first 2 miles.

1.9   High cliffs of pink and brown granite stand hundreds of feet above both sides of the canyon, marking the position of a great granite dike running northeast-southwest across the canyon. Road now climbs very steeply for a short distance.

2.2   Road intersection at forks of Willow Creek. Very poor jeep road goes to the left, along the north fork of the creek, to a small ranch several miles away. Road to mica mine turns right, following eastward up the canyon of the south fork.

2.9   Road passes above Precambrian rocks into overlying, flat-lying Mississippian and Pennsylvanian beds.

3.9   Good spring in small meadow to left of road.

4.2   Middle Pennsylvanian limestones and shales exposed here in roadcut are highly fossiliferous, containing numerous large brachiopods, particularly in some of the hard limestone layers. Corals, gastropods, and pelecypods can be found occasionally. Other fossiliferous layers at miles 4.4 and 5.2.

4.9   Big turn in road after small bridge. For about a mile, road climbs steeply along the side of a precipitous slope in a series of great, winding switchbacks.

5.2   Sharp bend in road, with several tens of feet of rock exposed. Sandstone cliffs showing small cavities due to dissolution of readily soluble limestone concretions. A tall plant growing along these cliffs, when in bloom

BRACHIOPOD.
Composita.

PELECYPOD.
Nucula.

late in June attracts hundreds of hummingbirds. From here are panoramic views of the lower canyon, passed earlier, but now far below, and the Santa Fe Range to the west.

6.1 Minor side road to left dead ends in about a mile; continue straight ahead.

6.7 Road intersection. Road to right (southwest) follows a level, wooded ridge to former site of an old fire lookout tower. Road ahead (southeast) goes down to the head of Cow Creek, where it ends. Richly fossiliferous Middle Pennsylvanian limestones are exposed along this road as it begins to descend steeply into Cow Creek. Take road to left (northeast) that ascends a long, gradual ridge, partly through open meadows, where after about a mile, you will have exceptional views of the Truchas Peaks.

7.9 Trail sign to left of road; unmaintained trail to Valle Medio.

8.7 Road climbs around the head of Cow Creek toward the East Divide. Bare round summit of Elk Mountain (11,600 ft) is the high point of the divide to the southeast.

9.6 Road junction. Road to right leads to top of Elk Mountain (1.8 miles), location of Forest Service radio repeater site. Take road to left to East Divide.

10.2 East Divide (11,400 ft). Signpost. Poor, unmaintained secondary road continues downslope to the east, passing broad, grassy meadows, and a fine spring halfway down. The road ends at abandoned mica mine after 2 miles. Many years ago, a primitive wagon road continued 5 miles down this same ridge south of Hollinger Canyon to the old Harvey ranch (see early chapters of *Beatty's Cabin*, by Elliott Barker).

D.H.MONEYPENNY.

HUMMINGBIRD.

SANTA FE RANGE.
View west across Pecos valley from East Divide.

The top of Elk Mountain is an easy hike half a mile upslope from this point. A good horseback trail runs north from here along the divide, forming the southeastern part of Sky Line trail, which extends nearly 50 miles around the rim of the upper Pecos drainage, providing many spectacular views, and connecting with various other trails (Trip 15).

HERMIT'S PEAK.
View east from the East Divide north of Elk Mountain.

The view from East Divide is superb—even more so from the summit of Elk Mountain: the wide, low plains country to the east; Hermit's Peak, with its massive, oddly arching shape; Storrie reservoir, far out toward Las Vegas; and the broad, green expanse of the lower Rociada Valley all stretch out into the far distance (see Oliver La Farge's *Behind the Mountains*, a delightful, authentic story of the early days in this beautiful valley). On a perfectly clear day, you can see 70 or 80 miles to the Great Plains on the eastern horizon. The top of the divide is held up by flat beds of Pennsylvanian sediments, but the contact with underlying Precambrian rocks is met again farther east about 1.5 miles downslope. Thus the mica mine, 2 miles downslope, occurs in the Precambrian, in a type of very coarse grained, light-colored granitic rock called pegmatite, in which large crystals of mica, feldspar, and quartz are commonly found. This mine, now abandoned, produced a small tonnage of mica during World War II.

Trip 11

HOLY GHOST CANYON TO
WEST DIVIDE (SANTA FE)

This trip commences from Holy Ghost Canyon, which diverges from the Pecos River about 6 miles south of Cowles and 13.7 miles north of Pecos. Especially advantageous to those based in the Terrero-Holy Ghost Canyon area and south, this trip affords the shortest access to fishing lakes and points of scenic interest along parts of the West (Santa Fe) Divide, including Spirit Lake, Stewart Lake, and Lake Katherine—as well as challenging ascents of the high rocky summits of Santa Fe Baldy, Penitente Peak, and Lake Peak. It may also be used to cross the West Divide and eventually reach the Santa Fe Ski Basin. After 3 miles it connects with Winsor trail, starting from Cowles. For a description of points beyond Winsor trail junction, see the description of Winsor Creek trail, Trip 12, beginning at 5.2 miles.

Trail begins at campground near end of road up Holy Ghost Canyon, 3.2 miles from bridge over Pecos River at Terrero, where road branches off from NM-63.

From the campground to Spirit Lake is 6 miles; walking time, 3 hours; riding time, 2½ hours. From the campground to the West Divide is 8 miles; walking time, 3¾ hours; riding time, 3 hours. From the campground to Lake Peak is 10.5 miles; walking time, about 6 hours.

0.0   Campground. Cross small bridge over Holy Ghost Creek near signpost.

0.3   Grassy flats by creek. Steep canyon is heavily timbered, generally concealing flat-lying beds of Middle Pennsylvanian sandstone, shale, and limestone.

0.6   Trail crosses creek to east bank.

1.1   Trail lies in timber 100 to 150 ft above river, above cliffs of Pennsylvanian sandstone, shale, and limestone.

1.3   Trail recrosses Holy Ghost Creek to west bank just above junction of two streams, where massive cliffs of flat-lying Pennsylvanian limestone can be seen. Trail ascends westward for some distance along north side of west tributary, then turns north, climbing high above Holy Ghost Creek.

2.0   Trail crosses creek twice, first to east, and then back to west bank, then continues almost due north about 60 to 80 ft above creek. Valley is narrow and mostly wooded, providing occasional glimpses of small outcrops of shale and limestone.

2.4   Trail crosses creek to east bank, beginning long, arduous climb north to reach top of high ridge between Holy Ghost and Winsor Creeks.

2.6   Blocks of coarse sandstone become common along trail; ledges are in place locally. The Middle Pennsylvanian sandstones here carry abundant angular grains of white to tan feldspar, in addition to glassy quartz grains, its chief constituents. This type of feldspar-rich sandstone is termed arkose; the feldspar indicates an origin derived from the weathering of granite. Inasmuch as granite makes up all of the high mountain country a mile or so westward, that area is presumed to have been the source of these quartz and feldspar grains, washed from ancient granite hills that rose westward above an ancient sea 200 million years ago in Middle Pennsylvanian time.

2.8   Slabby masses of black shale and limestone are locally in place above east side of trail. The bedding of these rocks (the layers of sediments as originally laid down flat in water) has been tilted up at an angle of about

CATCHES OF TROUT IN THE HIGH COUNTRY.

10 degrees. The beds strike due north and dip down 10 degrees to the east. This downward tilt to the east contrasts with the almost flat position of bedding already seen southeastward in the main canyon, and is caused by nearly vertical movement along the great fault three-quarters of a mile west. This fault separates granite on the west from Middle Pennsylvanian sedimentary rocks on the east. As sediments were dropped downward along the fault, granite moved upward; thus the Pennsylvanian beds close to the fault were dragged upward against the fault and tilted eastward at an increasingly steep angle as the fault is approached. In Holy Ghost Creek, 0.3 mile west of the trail at this point (nearer to the fault), strata have been observed dipping 53 degrees to the east. This great fault zone has been traced over 38 miles north-south. It is crossed, and described, in Trip 12, 13, and 14 (also see geology and trail map).

3.0　　Trail enters small meadow on summit of long ridge and joins Winsor Trail at signpost at west end of meadow (9,840 ft). For continuation of Winsor Creek trail to Spirit Lake, Santa Fe Divide, Lake Peak, and Lake Katherine, see Trip 12.

Trip 12

WINSOR CREEK TRAIL—
COWLES TO SPIRIT LAKE,
WEST (SANTA FE) DIVIDE
AND LAKE PEAK

Out of Cowles are two good riding and hiking trails to the many points of interest on the West Divide, such as Lake Katherine, Spirit Lake, Stewart Lake, Santa Fe Baldy, and Lake Peak. Winsor Creek trail starts from Winsor Creek campground, first following Winsor Creek, then climbing to the ridge top above the south side of Winsor Canyon by a gradual ascent. Winsor Ridge trail (Trip 13) starts above the north side of Winsor Creek road, a quarter of a mile west of Cowles, and climbs gradually westward on the high south-facing slope of Winsor Ridge, hundreds of feet above Winsor Canyon. The trails meet near the head of Winsor Creek, about one mile south of Stewart Lake. Distance to this junction is 6.5 miles on Winsor Creek trail, and 6 miles on Winsor Ridge trail. Both trails are equally good, but Winsor Creek trail is more gentle. Winsor Ridge trail is more scenic and a more direct route to Stewart Lake.

For convenience the trail to Spirit Lake and Lake Peak is described in this trip, and the trail to Lake Katherine, Santa Fe Baldy, and Stewart Lake is described in Trip 13, although the two trails follow a common route for almost one mile.

Winsor Creek trail begins at campground at end of road on Winsor Creek, 1.2 miles west of Cowles by road. Distances from this campground via this trail to the following points are approximately: Spirit Lake, 8.5 miles; riding time, 3 hours; walking time, 4 hours; Santa Fe Divide, 10 miles; riding time, 3½ hours; walking time, 4½ hours. Other distances via this trail: Lake Katherine, 9.5 miles; Stewart Lake, 7 miles.

0.0   Follow trail from Winsor Creek campground along the north bank of Winsor Creek.

0.8   Trail crosses Winsor Creek to south bank. After 400 ft, intersection with abandoned trail to Spirit Lake leading west along creek, while main trail doubles back to left and swings around southeast as it begins long, gentle eastward ascent of ridge. Old trail to Spirit Lake can be used only by experienced hikers (not by riders) needing a shortcut to Lake Katherine, a saving of one to two miles. Old trail continues west along creek for a short distance, then climbs rather steeply up ridge on south side of Winsor Canyon. After 3 miles, it intersects Winsor Creek trail one mile east of the junction of the two main trails at Winsor Creek. Deadfalls are numerous across this abandoned trail; it CANNOT be used by horses.

      From here on along main trail, outcrops and small cliffs can be seen, consisting of flat-lying beds of Middle Pennsylvanian sandstone, shale, and limestone. Trail goes through mixed conifer forests.

2.6   Trail reaches easternmost promontory of ridge summit above south side of Winsor Canyon. Limited views of Cowles and Pecos Canyon may be seen through the trees. Trail now swings around sharply to southwest and climbs gently westward through aspen and pine forests near top of ridge.

5.2   Signpost at west end of small meadow on summit of long ridge (9,840 ft).

Intersection with trail to Holy Ghost Canyon coming in from southeast (Trip 11). Trail continues northwest in trees, along northeast side of long ridge. For the next half a mile, loose blocks, as well as outcropping beds, of arkosic sandstones, shales, and limestones can be observed.

5.4   Good exposure of smooth, gray limestone next to trail. The bedding of this limestone (the layers of sediment as originally laid down flat in water) has been tilted down at an angle of about 20 degrees to the east. The beds strike due north. This downward tilt to the east contrasts with the nearly flat position of bedding eastward in Winsor Creek and southeastward in Holy Ghost Canyon. Steeper dips here are caused by almost vertical movement along a great fault that will be crossed 0.5 mile west. This fault separates granite on the west from Middle Pennsylvanian sedimentary strata on the east (see cross section). As sedimentary layers were dropped

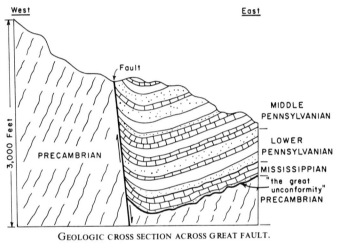

GEOLOGIC CROSS SECTION ACROSS GREAT FAULT.

downward along the fault, granite moved upward; thus, the Pennsylvanian beds close to the fault were dragged upward against the fault and tilted up westward at an increasingly steep angle as the fault is approached. Near this fault about one mile south of this trail, sedimentary strata east of the fault are tilted up westward as much as 53 degrees. This great fault zone has been traced over 38 miles north-south (geology and trail map). It is also crossed, and described, in Trips 13 and 14. Although the limestones are fossiliferous, good fossil collecting is not possible. The most abundant fossils present are small protozoans called *fusulinids,* about one-quarter inch in length with shells shaped like grains of wheat. Fusulinids are useful indicators in establishing the stratigraphic positions of beds in which they occur. Those found here, as well as other stratigraphic and paleontological evidence, show that these particular beds are high up in the Pennsylvanian sequence, at least 1,000 ft above the basal Mississippian limestone in contact with the great unconformity elsewhere (above). These fusulinid-

FUSULINID.
Fusulina.

bearing beds are in direct contact with Precambrian granite along the fault just ahead, not 1,000 ft above the Precambrian, as normally found; thus the Pennsylvanian beds have been dropped down at least this distance to account for their anomalous stratigraphic position. In this way, the total movement along a fault dislocation can be computed.

5.9   Brown granite sand appears abruptly, covering the ground and outcrops of brown and pink granite that occur slightly farther along the trail. Therefore, the fault contact between Precambrian granite and Pennsylvanian beds has been passed a few yards back. The exact fault contact cannot be seen because of soil cover, but its position on the trail can be ascertained within about 5 ft! See if you can find it. It is located near a large, crooked aspen tree (if the aspen is still there!) at the right of the trail.

6.1   Intersection with abandoned shortcut trail from Winsor Creek, coming in from east, below main trail. Trail soon crosses gully and swings east, then west, around a narrow, hummocky ridge made up of huge granite boulders. This ridge is a glacial side moraine running east-west along the south side of upper Winsor Canyon. The material in the moraine was transported eastward by glacial ice many thousands of years ago from granite cliffs to the west. (See discussion of glacial moraines north of Stewart Lake in latter part of Winsor Ridge trail description.)

6.5   Signpost on north bank of Winsor Creek (10,120 ft) and major intersection with Winsor Ridge trail (Trip 13) coming in from the right (north). This trail affords an excellent return route to Cowles. Sky Line trail is also met here, coinciding at first with Winsor Ridge trail at a point north of Stewart Lake, then separating to proceed northward to a junction near Johnson Lake, and on to Horsethief Meadows and Pecos Baldy (Trip 15).

SPIRIT LAKE.

BARE RIDGE OF PENITENTE PEAK (LEFT) AND SERRATED SUMMIT OF LAKE PEAK (CENTER SKY LINE).
View from crest of Santa Fe Baldy.

Follow trail to left, climbing westward above Winsor Creek toward Spirit Lake, West (Santa Fe) Divide, and Lake Katherine.

7.5   Signpost by meadow near Winsor Creek. Trail straight ahead continues west up Winsor Creek to Lake Katherine. Follow trail to left for Spirit Lake. Trail crosses Winsor Creek and climbs southward up broad but rocky trail past blocks of granite up to 12 ft in diameter.

8.3   Spirit Lake (10,809 ft). This lake, small in size, but grandly placed, with high granite walls towering above it on the west, is of glacial origin. Blocks of granite piled up at the east edge of the lake block the outlet. Glacial ice scooped out the lake depression and dammed its outlet with loose morainic rock debris. The lake is kept stocked with fish, and the fishing is excellent at times.

To reach the West (Santa Fe) Divide, follow trail past lake to southeast, gradually turning southwest, then west, staying at the same elevation. The forest is mostly corkbark fir and Douglas fir, with a few spruce.

10.0   Trail junction in forested spot on West Divide (11,050 ft). Unmarked trail to left, to the southwest, goes to Lake Peak (3 miles), and Santa Fe Lake (4.5 miles). At first, this trail climbs the west side of Penitente Peak, gradually topping a high ridge leading to the crest of this peak, and then fades out on the bare, rocky summit. After a sharp descent to the southwest, Lake Peak trail is picked up in the high, rocky saddle between Penitente Peak and Lake Peak. The head of the ski lift above Aspen Basin is only about 2 miles farther west by a good trail from Lake Peak.

Take trail straight ahead, westward, descending toward Aspen Basin (5 miles).

10.3   Puerto Nambé. Trail junction and signpost in beautiful, vast parklike meadow overlooking a panoramic landscape to the west, spanning the wide Rio Grande valley all the way to the Jemez Mountains. To the south rises the rocky summit of Lake Peak; next to it, to the southeast, stands the long, bare summit of Penitente Peak. To the north stretches the wide expanse of open grassy slopes leading upward to the main summit of Santa Fe Baldy. A sharp division between trees and open slopes running northward as far as the eye can see marks the extreme point of advance of the great forest fire of the 1870's. From this meadow a good horse trail leads west down the canyon, passing over a high ridge to the south (just east of Aspen Mountain) and eventually reaching the picnic ground near the ski lift in Aspen Basin.

Trail to northeast, the beginning of Sky Line trail (Trip 15), crosses the southeast ridge of Santa Fe Baldy, providing splendid views in all directions. Descending to Lake Katherine (3 miles), this trail continues on to Truchas Peaks and Santa Barbara Divide.

Trip 13

WINSOR RIDGE TRAIL—
COWLES TO LAKE KATHERINE
AND SANTA FE BALDY

Lake Katherine (11,700 ft) lies just below and east of the mighty summit ridge of Santa Fe Baldy. Regarded as the most beautiful high mountain lake of the upper Pecos region, a visit here makes an unusually fine scenic trip. Fishermen are attracted to this lake because it is kept stocked with trout. Stewart and Spirit Lakes are also favorite fishing spots.

Winsor Ridge trail is one of the two trails from Cowles to the many points of interest on the West Divide (see Trip 12 for alternate route via Winsor Creek). In addition to Lake Katherine and Santa Fe Baldy, this trail can be used to reach Stewart, Spirit, and Johnson Lakes, as well as Sky Line trail.

For convenience, the trail to Stewart Lake, Lake Katherine, and Santa Fe Baldy is described here; the route to Spirit Lake and Lake Peak is given in Trip 12. The two trails meet near the head of Winsor Creek; Winsor Creek trail provides a pleasant return route to Cowles.

The Winsor Ridge trail has a rather obscure beginning at the foot of the steep hillside a quarter of a mile west of Cowles, on the road up Winsor Creek. Winsor Ridge trail can also be reached from the road on the west side of Pecos River a quarter of a mile north of Cowles, just before the road reaches Los Pinos guest ranch.

Distances from the beginning of this trail are approximately: Stewart Lake, 5.5 miles; walking time, 2½ hours; riding time, 1¾ hours. Distance to Lake Katherine by this trail from the starting point is 9 miles; walking time, 4½ to 5 hours; riding time, 3½ to 4 hours.

0.0   Trail beginning on Winsor Creek road at signpost marked "Trails" climbs north hillside. Within 100 yards a trail to Winsor Creek campground branches to the left. Continue northward, upslope.

0.1   Second trail junction. Trail to right goes to Panchuela campground. Take Winsor Ridge trail to left, beginning a gradual ascent westward, on the north side of Winsor Canyon.

0.6   Trail swings around northeast, then back west again after 0.2 mile, in a large switchback, as trail climbs ridge slope gradually. Trail exposures and small cliffs of flat-lying beds of Middle Pennsylvanian sandstone, shale and limestone occur along the trail.

1.8   After ascending through dense aspen groves, trail crosses near head of steep tributary valley that cuts deeply into main canyon of Winsor Creek.

2.9   In open groves of aspen, note continuous ledge of Pennsylvanian limestone to right of trail dipping about 5 degrees west.

3.7   Trail crosses the head of a boggy creek, with open meadows extending upslope almost to the top of Winsor Ridge.

4.6   Trail passes through forests of mixed aspen and conifers broken by scattered grassy meadows, some providing superb views of the Santa Fe Range to the west.

5.1   Signpost in small meadow (10,210 ft) and trail junction with Sky Line trail (Trip 15). Trail to right, northward, is Sky Line trail going to trail junction near Johnson Lake then on to Horsethief Meadows. Take trail to left, southward, for Lake Katherine.

This trail junction is on Pennsylvanian shale, but to the southwest, within about 100 yards, are boulders of Precambrian granite marking the fault contact between Pennsylvanian sedimentary beds on the east and Precambrian granite on the west (see geology and trail map). From here on, westward and southwestward, all the way to the city of Santa Fe, the rock is mostly this same type of granite. This fault is the same great fault contact running north-south more than 38 miles; it is also crossed on Winsor Creek trail (Trip 12), 1 mile south, and on the trail from Cowles to Horsethief Meadows (Trip 14). The beds of Middle Pennsylvanian shale and sandstone in fault contact with brown Precambrian granite are beds normally more than 1,000 ft above the Mississippian limestone beds directly on top of the great erosion surface cut into Precambrian rocks. From the fossils present in beds tilted up against the granite nearby, paleontologists can tell where these beds belong in the stratigraphic sequence of Pennsylvanian sedimentary beds laid down, one on top of another, 250 million years ago in an ancient sea. (Unfortunately, the contact between the two types of rocks is obscured along this trail by vegetation and soil.) The evidence here indicates that vertical movement along this huge fault has dropped all the Pennsylvanian rocks downward more than 1,000 ft on the east side of the fault, the Precambrian granite having been uplifted high above the sedimentary beds on the west side of the fault. These clues assist geologists in piecing together parts of a story going back hundreds of millions of years in earth history (diagram, p. 79).

5.5   Trail to southwest passes a second large meadow, then reaches the wooded east end of Stewart Lake. This lake, a quarter of a mile long and

SANTA FE BALDY.
View from Winsor Ridge trail.

STEWART LAKE.
Spirit and Stewart Lakes, not far apart, have similar settings amid dense pine forests.

surrounded by spruce forest, mirrors in its still water the image of the high, rocky northeast peak of Santa Fe Baldy. A small artificial earth dam across the eastern outlet of the lake holds the lake at its present depth and position. At times, fishing is excellent, as the lake is kept stocked with trout.

Trail crosses dam, passes a trail to right that follows shore of lake, then descends southwest toward Winsor Creek. Trail here, and also north of Stewart Lake by large meadow, skirts or follows atop a narrow hummocky ridge (tens of feet high) of huge granite boulders. These east-west-trending ridges are parts of a glacial end moraine deposited from glacial ice that pushed eastward many thousands of years ago from granite cliffs to the west. Such piled-up morainic material may be responsible in part for damming upstream drainage over a wide area here along the east slope of the West Divide, and for creating such flat and scooped-out areas as are now occupied by Stewart and Spirit Lakes, and the several large meadows north of these lakes.

6.0   Major trail intersection and signs at Winsor Creek (10,120 ft). Winsor

CONEY.

Creek trail comes in from left, crossing from southeast bank of creek; an excellent return route to Cowles (Trip 12). Trail to Lake Katherine climbs straight ahead southwest up side of ridge along north bank of Winsor Creek by means of several small switchbacks. Follow this trail; it also leads to Spirit Lake and West (Santa Fe) Divide.

7.0   Trail junction and signpost near Winsor Creek (10,690 ft). Trail to south crosses Winsor Creek and goes to Spirit Lake (Trip 12). For Lake Katherine, follow trail to right ascending steeply westward up ridge. Trail is rocky with much granite rubble and makes many switchbacks, climbing over 1,000 ft in a distance of less than 2.5 miles.

8.5   After climbing 2 miles up boulder ridge to northwest, trail swings across ridge to west under high cliffs of gray granite forming east shoulder of the northeast peak of Santa Fe Baldy. To the south, across the head of Winsor drainage, rises the long southwest summit ridge of Santa Fe Baldy. Trail now heads out into open area of great granite boulders near the head of Winsor Creek.

9.0   Lake Katherine is reached after the trail climbs the steep side and over the crest of the rocky, ridge-forming glacial moraine that dams the lake. This blue-green lake, about a third of a mile across, has a remarkably beautiful setting. Towering walls of tan granite 1,000 ft high surround it on all sides, except around the eastern entrance. The lake, of glacial origin, lies at an altitude of 11,700 ft. Spruce trees grow thinly around the lake, and alpine flowers of all kinds bloom in profusion among the great boulders. The lake is kept stocked with trout, therefore may offer excellent fishing. Large marmots and small coneys are commonly seen by the lake. Lake Katherine is named after the late Katherine Chavez Kavanagh (formerly of Los Pinos guest ranch, Cowles) who blazed and cleared the first trail to it about 60 years ago.

Lake Katherine.

ON THE WAY TO THE SUMMIT OF SANTA FE BALDY.

Sky Line trail (Trip 15) continues to left (southwest), leading to the Santa Fe Ski Basin (7 miles). At first, trail follows boulder ridge skirting lake on east; after 2 miles, it crosses high saddle on southeast shoulder of Santa Fe Baldy. This is a steep, rocky trail for horses.

Although the summit of Santa Fe Baldy stands a full 1,000 ft above the lake, the climb is easy for hikers. The easiest route is by way of the steep grassy slope ascending above the north side of the lake to a low ridge. This east-west ridge connects the northeast peak with the small knob at the north end of the main north-south summit ridge. From this small knob, at about 12,000 ft, the half-mile, 500-ft climb along the summit ridge south to the highest peak is gradual. A large cairn of rocks marks the top, as does a U.S. Geological Survey bench mark (inexcusably defaced beyond recognition). From here are magnificent views in every direction: the Jemez Range westward across the broad Rio Grande valley; Lake Peak to the south; Pecos valley to the east; and Capulin Peak, Pecos Baldy, and Truchas Peaks to the north.

Trip 14

miles 7
hours 3½

COWLES TO CAVE CREEK
AND HORSETHIEF MEADOWS

The excellent and easy trail described here is one of the most pleasant short trips in the Cowles area. Some interesting caves are visited, and wild flowers are abundant during much of the summer season.

Trail begins either at a small bridge over Panchuela Creek, at north end of the Panchuela campground; at the end of the road on the west side of the Pecos River, 1.5 miles north of Cowles; or on the hillside opposite the gate of Panchuela ranger station, on the road 1.3 miles north of Cowles.

From the campground to Horsethief Meadows is 5.5 miles; walking time, 2½ hours; riding time, 2 hours.

0.0   Panchuela Campground. Trail crosses small bridge to east side of Panchuela Creek; flat-lying, fossiliferous Early Pennsylvanian beds of dark shale and limestone occur in bluff above bridge.

0.3   Trail from Panchuela ranger station crosses Panchuela Creek from west side, in open meadow. Trail continues north on east side of creek.

0.8   Pecos Wilderness boundary sign and trail junction. Trail to right, Dockwiller trail, goes to upper Jacks Creek and eventually to Pecos Baldy Lake (Trip 6). Take trail straight ahead, up Panchuela Creek to Horsethief Meadows.

1.5   Trail crosses Panchuela Creek and turns west up Cave Creek. Loose

CAVES ON CAVE CREEK.

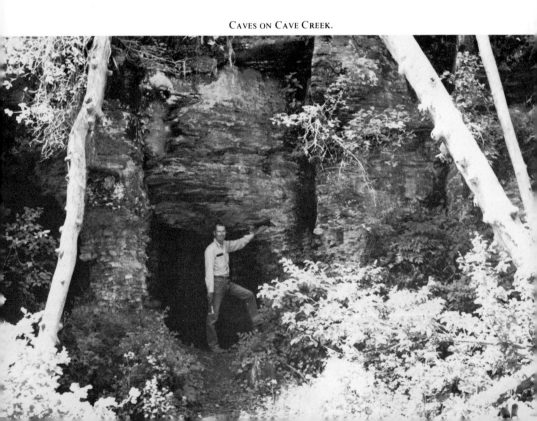

blocks of thick-bedded Early Pennsylvanian sandstone occur along trail. Shale beds and thin limestone layers in small bluff above sign are moderately fossiliferous.

2.0   Stream swings to left away from trail, and dry creek bed appears along trail. From this point on, watch for caves in cliffs of thin-bedded Middle Pennsylvanian limestone on south bank of stream 200 yards farther on. Half the stream goes underground via two caves, and may contribute to springs farther downstream on Cave Creek. This stream may also be the source of springs in the Cowles area. The caves were formed as water entered fractures in the soluble limestone; the fractures were enlarged to caves as the limestone dissolved over many years. Here, limestone strata dip southward at 10 degrees; the stream flows along the limestone beds parallel to their dip, and the caves extend back into the cliffs for some distance.

2.1   Beyond caves, trail climbs high above creek. Large blocks of thick-bedded Middle Pennsylvanian sandstone and conglomerate appear on trail.

3.7   Where small gully with rivulet crosses trail from north, the stream changes its course from nearly east-west to north-south, and trail veers around parallel to the stream. The great fault zone, running north-south more than 38 miles, crosses trail in this vicinity (crossed also on Trips 12 and 13). Here the fault separates Precambrian granite on the west from Middle Pennsylvanian strata on the east. The Pennsylvanian beds are poorly exposed and are probably turned up steeply so as to dip down eastward away from the fault, but this cannot be observed here. The Middle Pennsylvanian beds have been dropped downward and tilted down eastward along the east side of the fault, whereas the Precambrian granite has been uplifted on the west side of the fault, relative to those down-dropped Paleozoic beds against which the granite is now in contact. The total up-down displacement is more than 1,000 ft (based on observations in nearby areas of the stratigraphic position of the Pennsylvanian beds) here in direct contact with Precambrian basement rocks, but normally lying this vertical distance above the Precambrian. The fault surface is nearly vertical where cutting across these rocks along this part of Cave Creek (see the geology and trail map for location of heavy black line marking this great fault; note up-down movement along fault as shown in diagram, p. 79).

3.9   Signpost and trail junction with Sky Line trail, coming in from left (south) after crossing Cave Creek. Trail in that direction passes near Johnson Lake and leads on to Stewart Lake (Trip 15). Take trail straight ahead, along Cave Creek, for Horsethief Meadows. This trail now is part of Sky Line trail.

4.3   Trail leaves Cave Creek and makes steep climb, almost due north, out of Cave Creek Valley. Several switchbacks wind through great loose masses of gray granite and white to tan granite pegmatite full of coarse patches of quartz and feldspar.

4.8   Trail tops small divide (10,125 ft) dotted with aspens and small grassy meadows. Large blue columbines (color plate 2, bottom), one of the most beautiful of all alpine flowers, are usually common in this area in July, along with reddish-purple shooting stars and a host of colorful companions, especially plentiful along the early part of this trail.

5.5   After descending slope north of small divide, trail intersects a small tributary creek leading downward to the broad grassy flats of Horsethief

BLUE COLUMBINE.

Meadows. Signpost in meadows on north bank of Horsethief Creek. Sky Line trail, to Pecos Baldy Lake, turns right (east), down the valley (Trip 15). Secondary trail to left follows broad meadows northward up valley for about half a mile before climbing northwestward over the Main Divide. Trail descends west slope of Main Divide, eventually leading to Panchuela West ranger cabin and connecting with trail northward to the old Brazos cabinsite and the big canyon of the Rio Medio draining the west slope of the Sangre de Cristo Range. Abundant broken pieces (shards) of pottery,

HORSETHIEF MEADOWS.
View southwest to Capulin Peak.

dated about A.D. 1500, have been found in spots on the Main Divide between Horsethief Creek and Panchuela West.

Here, Horsethief Valley runs north-south, this trend being determined by its location along the great north-south fault zone (mentioned earlier) separating Precambrian granite on the west from Pennsylvanian sediments on the east, creating a line of major structural weakness in the rocks. On the west side of the valley, small bluffs of tan granite are well exposed in various places from the trail intersection northward.

Obsidian artifacts have been found in Horsethief Meadows, suggesting that Indians camped in this pleasant valley many hundreds of years ago.

According to tales still told, this isolated grassy valley was a secret hideout for holding horses stolen from ranches in the foothills far to the south and east—hence the name, Horsethief Meadows. Such horses were allegedly rebranded in the meadows, then taken west over the Main Divide to be sold in the Rio Grande valley.

Trip 15

miles 48
3 days

SKY LINE TRAIL

The most challenging trail in the upper Pecos is Sky Line trail, beginning on the West (Santa Fe) Divide, near Aspen Basin, and extending as a great horseshoe around the entire upper Pecos drainage basin, a trail distance of about 48 miles. On the way, it passes Santa Fe Baldy, Pecos Baldy, the Truchas Peaks, and Santa Barbara Divide, finally culminating at the East Divide by Elk Mountain. This trail provides seemingly endless, incomparable views of breathtaking mountain scenery. It also affords an overall view of the many interesting aspects of the regional geology. Refer to the geology and trail map frequently to keep your bearings both geographically and geologically!

Traversing the entire trail takes several days. For convenience of description, the trip is subdivided into the following sections:

1—West (Santa Fe) Divide to Pecos Baldy Lake; about 17 miles.
2—Truchas Peaks area, from Pecos Baldy Lake to Chimayosos Peak; about 7.5 miles.
3—Santa Barbara Divide, from Chimayosos Peak to Gascon Point; about 10 miles.
4—East (Elk Mountain) Divide, from Gascon Point to Elk Mountain; about 13.5 miles.

The Sky Line trail, particularly in the first section on the West Divide, coincides with parts of other described trips. Refer to the map to see where various trips coincide; then select the trail that best suits your purposes.

1—West (Santa Fe) Divide to Pecos Baldy Lake

The first section of Sky Line trail includes Lake Katherine, Stewart Lake, a junction near Lake Johnson, Cave Creek, Horsethief Meadows, and Pecos Baldy Lake.

The trail begins at trail junction and signpost in Puerto Nambé, on Winsor trail, about half a mile west of the West Divide. The beginning of the trail is only 4 miles by trail from the end of the road at Santa Fe Ski Basin. The starting point can also be reached from Pecos valley, either via Holy Ghost Canyon trail (Trip 11), Winsor Creek trail (Trip 12), or Winsor Ridge trail (Trip 13).

From Puerto Nambé to Lake Katherine is 3 miles; walking time, 1½ hours; riding time, 1¼ hours. From Puerto Nambé to Horsethief Meadows is about 11 miles; walking time, 5 hours; riding time, 4 hours. The distance to Pecos Baldy Lake on the Sky Line trail is about 17 miles; walking time (not including stops!), about 8 hours; riding time, 6½ hours.

0.0 From signpost in Puerto Nambé (10,940 ft) follow trail northeast toward saddle on southeast ridge of Santa Fe Baldy. Trail crosses open meadows with few stunted trees and ascends ridge in a series of gentle switchbacks. Blocks of granite are scattered along the trail.

1.1 Trail reaches saddle (11,620 ft) on ridge southeast of Santa Fe Baldy. In addition to continual views to the west, are views east to Pecos valley and northeast to Pecos Baldy.

From this saddle, the trail descends the extremely steep southwest side of the southernmost of the two glacial cirques on the east side of Santa Fe Baldy in a series of precipitous switchbacks. This steep northeast-facing slope, where deep snow drifts accumulate, is commonly snow covered until late June. This section of the trail may remain impassable to horses until July. (Ask the Forest Service about the condition of this part of the trail if you wish to use it during June.)

PUERTO NAMBÉ AND BEGINNING OF SKY LINE TRAIL.
View south to Penitente and Lake Peaks.

From the base of the steep slope, the trail goes north along the base of the cirque, skirting the very steep ridge of granite extending due east from the top of Santa Fe Baldy and separating the two cirques, then passes between great blocks of granite. The floor of the cirque is partly timbered. Lake Katherine lies at the head of the northern cirque.

3.0 Lake Katherine (11,700 ft). For a description of Lake Katherine and Santa Fe Baldy see Trip 13, the Winsor Ridge trail. For the first half a mile from the lake, the trail (same as Winsor Ridge trail) drops steeply eastward down the side of the ridge-forming glacial moraine that dams the lake (passing blocks of granite up to 8 ft in diameter), via a series of switchbacks. Trail then passes a small lake and goes eastward near base of great granite cliffs rising to the northeast ridge of Santa Fe Baldy. Trail then continually drops in elevation southeastward down the granite boulder slope on north side of Winsor Creek. A series of switchbacks periodically brings the trail near Winsor Creek.

5.0 Trail junction and signpost near Winsor Creek (10,690 ft). Trail to right (south) goes to Spirit Lake (Trip 12). Follow trail straight ahead, continuing eastward on north side of Winsor Creek. Partly by a series of steep switchbacks, trail drops down steep granite rubble slope through forests of mixed scrubby conifers.

6.0 Trail junction and signpost on northwest side of Winsor Creek (10,120 ft). Trail to right (southeast) is Winsor Creek trail (Trip 12), crossing Winsor Creek and continuing east to Cowles. Take trail to left (north) to Stewart Lake, for both Winsor Ridge trail (Trip 13) to Cowles and Sky Line trail. Rocky trail goes north, climbing gradually over hummocky ridges composed of glacially derived granite blocks.

6.5 Stewart Lake (10,232 ft). For a description of this lake, see Winsor Ridge

LAKE KATHERINE.

trail (Trip 13). Trail goes northeast, past small lake and boggy meadows, and some granite boulder terrain.

6.9   Trail junction and signpost (10,210 ft). Trail to right is Winsor Ridge trail to Cowles. This trail junction is on talus of Pennsylvanian sandstone and shale, but beginning about 100 yards to the southwest, on the trail to Stewart Lake, are granite boulders. The trail has crossed the large fault separating Precambrian granite on the west from Pennsylvanian sedimentary rocks on the east (geology and trail map). Significance of this fault is discussed in Trip 13, p. 84. Northward along Sky Line trail from this junction, this major fault is crossed again to the west side, back to granite, in about 0.3 mile. The trail northward follows the slope of the topography, climbing very little in elevation, with a rise in slope westward and a drop eastward. Once the fault is crossed again, many large granite blocks are along the trail, resulting in a rugged, irregular terrain.

7.7   Trail crosses fast stream, a southern tributary of Rito Oscuro. North of stream, trail swings northwest.

8.0   Trail junction and signpost (10,350 ft) on granite boulder ridge less than 0.1 mile north of where trail crosses Rito Oscuro (Spanish: hidden; in the shade).

Side trail to left dead-ends at Lake Johnson (11,100 ft), a beautiful small lake 2 miles northwest; half a mile beyond, Capulin Peak rises over 1,300 ft above the lake. The trail to the lake makes an almost continuous climb of about 750 ft over a good but fairly steep trail, with switchbacks through rough terrain of loose blocks of granite and forests of mixed conifers.

From junction, Sky Line trail turns right (northeast) and begins a long, gentle descent into Cave Creek. The trail continues through rough, timbered terrain, with an exceptional amount of old down timber (not on the trail!) in the first mile.

9.3   Trail junction and signpost (9,760 ft) after crossing to north side of Cave

Creek. Trail to right, down Cave Creek, is to Cowles. Take trail to left, up Cave Creek. From this junction to Horsethief Meadows, Sky Line trail coincides with a segment of Trip 14. A more detailed discussion is included there. Trail continues climbing northwestward, on the northeast side of Cave Creek.

9.7   Trail leaves Cave Creek, climbing steeply northward out of Cave Creek Valley, with several switchbacks among large granite boulders.

10.2   Trail crosses small divide (10,125 ft), descending due north through dense spruce and fir forests.

10.9   Horsethief Meadows. Trail junction and signpost on north side of Horsethief Creek. Arrow to left points upstream toward secondary trail to Panchuela West. Horsethief Meadows, extending along the valley for 1.5 miles both up and downstream from trail junction, has many excellent campsites. See Trip 14 for additional comments about Horsethief Meadows.

For Sky Line trail, turn right, downstream, Pecos Baldy Lake is 6 miles away. Trail stays on north side of creek, going through broad open meadows. It leaves the meadows and begins climbing northward about 0.8 mile southeast of trail junction. This turning point is obscure; watch carefully for blazes where the trail enters the trees. Avoid dropping down to creek level on secondary trails leading to campsites.

11.7   Trail enters trees on north side of Horsethief Valley and climbs steeply up side of valley. For next 3 miles, trail has several exceptionally steep stretches, not because terrain is so steep, but trail follows the maximum angle of slope. Trail begins in forests of mixed spruce, fir, and aspen.

11.9   Exceptional log fence built of logs the size of telephone poles, with a gate on the trail. Trail now angles more gently eastward around nose of southeast-sloping ridge, through dense forest of spruce and fir. Pennsylvanian sandstone rubble scattered along trail. After about a mile trail rounds nose of ridge and swings northwest, climbing steeply at first and then descending rather steeply into the upper reaches of Panchuela Creek.

13.2   Trail crosses Panchuela Creek, here a small, fast-flowing stream in dense forest of conifers. From creek, trail climbs northeast along a south-facing timbered slope, through much Pennsylvanian sandstone and conglomerate rubble on trail.

14.9   Trail junction and signpost (10,700 ft) in broad, open meadow providing first good view of Pecos Baldy to north. Trail straight ahead crosses Rito Perro and continues on to Jacks Creek, connecting with trails to Cowles. Take Sky Line trail to left for Pecos Baldy Lake. This trail heads up meadow, then shortly goes almost due north up ridge, through open forests and beautiful small meadows, toward Pecos Baldy. Pennsylvanian sandstone rubble is on trail.

15.8   Trail turns northeast and crosses Rito Perro, here a small, fast stream. Shortly before reaching the stream, you will see Precambrian quartzite blocks on the trail, indicating the crossing of the large fault heading around the east side of Pecos Baldy (geology and trail map). Trail now climbs north, then east, leaving headwaters of Rito Perro and passing along base of rubble slopes of glassy white quartzite along south side of the broad saddle stretching between East and West Pecos Baldy Peaks. Intermittently, there are interesting views up to the saddle. Trail ascends steep quartzite rubble ridge eastward. Snowdrifts may remain along this part of trail until late June.

16.4   Trail emerges into high, open grassy saddle (11,870 ft) on ridge extending southward from East Pecos Baldy. This vantage point provides one of the most spectacular, never-to-be-forgotten views in the entire upper Pecos area (frontispiece). Pecos Baldy Lake lies directly below, in the steep southeast-facing cirque; northward, the depression in the ridge north of the lake frames Truchas Peaks.

The large fault that swings around the east side of Pecos Baldy (geology and trail map) is actually exposed and can be examined along the steep eastern face of Pecos Baldy at the western edge of the saddle. In the saddle, you stand on Pennsylvanian shale, and the whole of the ridge extending southeast is composed of Pennsylvanian strata. Walk west in the saddle to base of steep slope of white quartzite. Examine the surface carefully. Locally, remnants of Pennsylvanian sandstone slabs dip almost vertically along the fault. Along the fault surface are grooves where rocks scraped against each other as displacement occurred. For additional discussion of this fault and its significance, see Trip 5 and diagram on p. 55.

From this saddle, unmarked trail to left (west) goes to the top of East Pecos Baldy (12,529 ft) by means of a well-engineered trail. Take trail to right (east), descending steep northeast side of timbered ridge facing Pecos Baldy Lake. There are numerous switchbacks, and blocks of Pennsylvanian sandstone can be seen along trail. Deep snowdrifts shaded by the forests may block parts of this section of the trail into late June.

17.0   Trail junction and signpost on broad ridge of terminal glacial moraine that dams Pecos Baldy Lake. Trail to right goes to Jacks Creek and Cowles (Trips 5 and 6). Sky Line trail continues eastward, around south side of lake, climbing Bordo Lajado northward toward Truchas Peaks. For additional discussion of Pecos Baldy Lake see Trip 5.

2—TRUCHAS PEAKS AREA, FROM PECOS BALDY LAKE TO CHIMAYOSOS PEAK

The second section of Sky Line trail includes a hike or ride along the crest of Bordo Lajado (Spanish: ridge in rock layers or layered ridge), the broad, grassy ridge stretching north from Pecos Baldy Lake to the foot of South Truchas Peak, and provides incomparable views in all directions. This trail provides, at the north end of Bordo Lajado, the easiest approach for climbing South Truchas Peak. From that point, Sky Line trail drops down the ridge side, hugs the east base of South Truchas Peak, and proceeds northward to Truchas Lakes. From there it continues northward to the west end of Santa Barbara Divide at Chimayosos Peak.

From Pecos Baldy Lake to the top of South Truchas Peak is 4.5 miles; walking time, about 4 hours (not a trip for horses!). From Pecos Baldy Lake to the Truchas Lakes is 6 miles; walking time, 3½ hours; riding time, 2½ hours. From Pecos Baldy Lake to Chimayosos Peak is 7.5 miles; walking time, 4¼ hours; riding time, 3 hours.

BORDO LAJADO, WITH TRUCHAS AND CHIMAYOSOS PEAKS ON SKYLINE.

17.0   Sky Line trail goes northeast from junction at Pecos Baldy Lake, and angles up ridge that forms the southern part of Bordo Lajado, through scattered fir and spruce trees.

17.6   Trail junction and signpost, half way up slope. Trail to right maintains constant elevation proceeding northeast to Beatty's Flats and Santa Barbara Divide via Rito Azul. Take trail to left, making steep ascent northward to saddle on ridge.

18.0   Southernmost rock monument, in saddle between two high points on southern part of broad, grassy Bordo Lajado. This open ridge, stretching from Pecos Baldy on the southwest to the south slope of South Truchas on the north, about 2.5 miles as the crow flies, is composed of flat-lying Pennsylvanian sandstone, shale, and limestone. These sedimentary rocks lie east of the great fault separating them from Precambrian quartzite that makes up both Pecos Baldy and Truchas Peaks (geology and trail map). From this point the trail heads north near the crest of the divide. Spectacular views are continually seen in all directions, particularly of Truchas Peaks to the north, but also of the Rio Grande valley to the west and the entire upper Pecos drainage basin to the east.

19.4   Point on trail opposite high point on grassy divide. Going north, the trail maintains a constant elevation and swings around the west side of the highest knob on the divide, located about half way between Pecos Baldy and South Truchas. By climbing about 120 ft in elevation to the top of this open knob (11,979 ft), you get a particularly fine view down the precipitous, horizontally stratified, east-facing side of Bordo Lajado.

20.1   Trail junction and signpost in grassy saddle immediately south of little South Truchas Peak. Trail downslope to west is main pack trail descending Rio Medio, eventually reaching the road east of Cordova. Trail downslope to east is Sky Line trail to Truchas Lakes.

The divide at this point (11,630 ft) provides the best and least steep approach for climbing to the top of South Truchas Peak (13,103 ft). In elevation, the climb is almost 1,500 ft. The summit is only 1.5 miles north of the saddle, but it is a long, hard climb (not for horses!) that seems much farther. Walk along top of broad ridge sloping up toward the north. After a quarter of a mile you pass a fault separating Pennsylvanian beds downslope and southeast from Precambrian rocks upslope and northwest. This fault is a continuation of the same great, almost vertical, fault encountered at Pecos Baldy Lake farther south (Trip 5). For another quarter of a mile, the ridge traverses a schist zone in quartzite, in which interesting specimens of gray, biotite-banded feldspathic gneiss, muscovite schist, and dark, hornblende-rich amphibolite can be observed. Beyond this zone, quartzite makes up the sharp knob of Little South Truchas Peak. Climb over the top of this small peak. Beyond is a deep saddle between this smaller peak and the main summit of South Truchas. The saddle consists of another schist and gneiss zone similar to the first one. These zones are about 750 ft across, and are soft enough for erosion to have carved low saddles in them. Beyond this second zone is nothing but hard, glassy, resistant quartzite all the way to the main summit. Trail plays out among loose talus blocks on steep uphill slope, but slightly below the sharp ridge crest on the west side, the route all the way to the top is good and secure.

Ahead to the north, another low saddle drops off between this summit and the east peak of Middle Truchas. This depression in the summit ridge is likewise made up of gneisses and schists that do not resist erosion as well as hard quartzite. A striking white micaceous quartzite, in which orange gar-

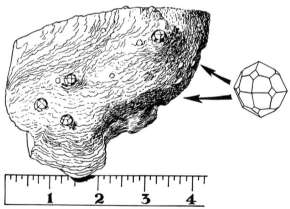

GARNET CRYSTALS IN MICACEOUS QUARTZITE (*scale in inches*).

net crystals of good size occur sparsely, makes up most of the east peak of Middle Truchas. Because of its whiteness, this peak can be seen fully 20 miles away.

Here at the summit (13,103 ft) you stand on the second highest point in New Mexico (Wheeler Peak, north of Taos, exceeds this by 50 ft); the views in all directions are incomparable. You feel as if you were on top of the world; no higher summits are visible (color plate 7, bottom). To the west, the entire vast stretch of the Rio Grande valley; to the north, the high east and west summits (the west peak, at 13,066 ft, is slightly higher than

MIDDLE AND NORTH TRUCHAS PEAKS.
View north from summit of South Truchas Peak. Taos Range on distant skyline.

the east) of Middle Truchas, with the massive crest of North Truchas (13,024 ft) just beyond these, followed slightly northeastward by the rounded, scarred knob of Chimayosos Peak. Eastward stretches the great world of the upper Pecos. To the south, the long, flat ridge top of Bordo Lajado connects with the huge mass of Pecos Baldy, beyond which, in the far distance southward, rise the granite summits of Santa Fe Baldy and Lake Peak. DO NOT CLIMB OR REMAIN ON THIS LOFTY PEAK DURING THUNDERSTORMS!

To continue north on Sky Line trail from the trail junction at the north end of Bordo Lajado, take the trail northeast angling down the ridge side.

20.5 At the base of the steep, open slope is an unmarked trail junction. The secondary unmaintained trail to the right heads down into the trees northeastward, intersecting the Rito Azul trail to Truchas Lakes (Trip 7) after about a mile. Sky Line trail turns north along base of divide, passing talus of Pennsylvanian shale and sandstone. After about a quarter of a mile the great fault is crossed, indicated by the sudden change on the trail to Precambrian quartzite talus. From this point northward trail follows fault trace closely, but Precambrian quartzite predominates, because rock debris of this type rolls down the slope eastward from South Truchas Peak, covering the fault and most of the softer Pennsylvanian strata. The trail passes several beautiful small meadows, with clear streams and countless red primroses (color plate 3, bottom). From some of the meadows are breathtaking views up the steep rocky slopes westward to South Truchas Peak, so close at hand. Several delightful campsites are available along this part of the trail.

21.7 Trail swings eastward around a precipitous narrow quartzite ridge jutting east-southeast from the main summit of South Truchas Peak. For a few tens of yards there is an abrupt drop-off on the east side of the trail; therefore, care must be taken with saddle and pack horses.

22.0   Trail drops northward after passing the steep ridge and crosses a small stream just east of a little lake. After 0.1 mile, trail passes east of a circular, boggy meadow surrounded by trees. These little meadows and valleys nestle high against the slope of Truchas Peaks and you forget how far below Pecos valley lies!

22.5   Trail junction with trail from Rito Azul to Truchas Lakes (Trip 7). Turn left (north) for Truchas Lakes.

In the area of this trail junction you can find rare and interesting mineral specimens (description, p. 61). From here the trail climbs rather steeply northward for the next 0.4 mile, through beautiful, partly open meadows, with views of the high peaks.

23.1   Truchas Lakes (11,900 ft). For a description of these beautiful lakes see Trip 7 (also color plate 1).

From the south side of the lower of the Truchas Lakes, Sky Line trail heads northeast along the base of North Truchas Peak. The trail is good but rocky, going over and around partly timbered talus slopes of white quartzite blocks.

CHIMAYOSOS PEAK FROM SKY LINE TRAIL.
Trail to Santa Barbara Valley (West Fork) can be seen skirting mountainside.

24.2   Signpost and trail junction (11,680 ft) located a short distance west of the draw leading up to the saddle between North Truchas and Chimayosos Peaks. From the open slopes near this junction are truly magnificent views of all three Truchas Peaks (color plates 2 and 3, top). No other vantage point in the upper Pecos provides such spectacular closeup views of these towering peaks.

Trail to right, downslope, cuts across the middle upper parts of tributaries of Rito de los Chimayosos to main trail junction on the divide between that drainage and Rito Azul (Trip 7). This trail is one of the routes to Beatty's Flats.

For Sky Line trail, continue east toward the south slope of Chimayosos Peak.

24.5   Trail junction and signpost (11,800 ft) on southwest slope of Chimayosos Peak. Trail to left ascends northwest and passes over the saddle between North Truchas and Chimayosos Peaks, leading to the West Fork of Santa Barbara Valley. Sky Line trail continues straight ahead across south slope of Chimayosos Peak.

All the way from Truchas Lakes the trail has continued on Precambrian quartzite, but has closely paralled the big fault located a short distance downslope (geology and trail map).

3—Santa Barbara Divide, from Chimayosos Peak to Gascon Point

The third section of Sky Line trail encompasses Santa Barbara Divide, proceeding from the south slope of Chimayosos Peak, on the west, to Gascon Point on the east. This divide marks the northern limit of the Pecos drainage basin. In contrast to other parts of the Sky Line trip, here the divide is oriented mostly east-west, connecting the north-south-trending Truchas Range with the similarly north-south-trending East Divide (or Elk Mountain Range). This change to an east-west orientation is partly due to the fact that now the great north-south-trending fault, with its associated north-south line of high quartzite peaks on the west, has been crossed and the attendant topography-controlling north-south linear element lost. (See fault-zone trace in north-central part of geology and trail map, at east margin of Chimayosos Peak.)

Santa Barbara Divide is in the most remote part of the Pecos Wilderness; here one can find solitude more readily than in the better known, more accessible parts of the Wilderness.

The trail junction at the beginning of this Sky Line trail segment is important because it marks the termination of the much-used trail from the north, along the West Fork of Santa Barbara River, beginning at the Santa Barbara campground (12 miles). This trail is good, and Santa Barbara Valley is one of the most beautiful in the entire Sangre de Cristo range, with several great meadows and superb views of Chimayosos Peak (color plate 6, top). Santa Barbara Valley, with the town of Peñasco at its northern end, provides an excellent access route for entering the Pecos Wilderness Area from the north.

The West Fork of Santa Barbara River is interesting geologically because it follows several miles along the major fault marking the eastern margin of Truchas Range. Great cliffs of Precambrian quartzite rise on the west side of that valley; less resistant Pennsylvanian rocks, with their more gentle topography, on the east (color plate 5, bottom).

Although Santa Barbara Divide is within the Pecos Wilderness Area, it forms the boundary between Santa Fe National Forest to the south and Carson National Forest to the north.

Camping sites are not available along the elevated and exposed Santa Barbara Divide, except near the east end, where excellent camping spots may be found by dropping about half a mile south into either the upper Valdez or upper Mora Valleys (see geology and trail map).

From the Chimayosos Peak trail junction to Gascon Point, on the East Divide, is about 10 miles; walking time, 5 hours; riding time, 4 hours.

24.5   Sky Line trail continues eastward from junction with trail north to West Fork of Santa Barbara River, climbing obliquely upward around the broad, mostly open south slope of Chimayosos Peak. This slope is white to light buff because of the Precambrian quartzite talus.

25.4   Trail junction and signpost on southeast slope of Chimayosos Peak. Rito del Padre trail descends southward, providing a direct route to Beatty's Flats (6 miles). Take Sky Line trail to left, swinging northward and slightly upward, toward saddle east of Chimayosos Peak.

25.5   Trail crosses covered trace of major fault, going from Precambrian quartzite (on west) to Pennsylvanian limestone and shale (to east). East of the fault, layers of limestone dip steeply eastward.

25.9   Trail has climbed to within a short distance of lowest point on saddle (12,060 ft), but stays slightly below the crest, on the south side of the divide. From this saddle a spectacular view unfolds northward down a branch of the West Fork of the Santa Barbara River.

The whole of the Santa Barbara Divide is composed of almost flat-lying Pennsylvanian sandstone and shale, with a few thin fossiliferous limestones. The rounded sandstone peaks to the east and northeast have a more subdued topographic expression compared to the higher mountains to the west, composed of Precambrian quartzite. The trace of the major fault separating the two rock sequences is best seen on the high east slope of Chimayosos Peak; the contact can be seen from this saddle, looking westward to the peak (color plate 5, top). The quartzite at the top of the peak is white to buff, but the Pennsylvanian rocks are brownish. The latter are sharply folded and steeply dipping near the fault, but flatten out eastward within half a mile. The structural relations here are similar to those a few miles southwest at Pecos Baldy Lake (diagram and photo, p. 55).

Sky Line trail continues eastward from near low point on saddle, passing cliffs of coarse Pennsylvanian sandstone and conglomerate. Frequent spectacular views lie in all directions, particularly back toward Truchas Peaks and south across the Pecos drainage basin. Trail skirts south side of Jicarilla Peak, a small, rather sharp-pointed peak (12,515 ft) composed chiefly of Pennsylvanian sandstones, and the first comparatively high point east

UPPER PECOS DRAINAGE BASIN FROM WEST SANTA BARBARA DIVIDE.
Great meadows atop Hamilton Mesa seen in middle distance and Elk Mountain on distant skyline.

of Chimayosos Peak. Trail is open, except for a few stunted Engelmann's spruce, and stays at a constant elevation.

27.1   Trail swings into the saddle immediately east of Jicarilla Peak, at the head of the middle fork of the Santa Barbara River. There is an excellent view of Jicarita Peak, about 6 miles north, as one looks down the valley of the middle Santa Barbara. Jicarita, the highest mountain in the region composed of flat-lying layers of Pennsylvanian sandstone and shale, has a square-shaped peak, reaching an elevation of 12,835 ft. At this point the divide drops steeply northward into the Santa Barbara drainage, but is more gentle on the Pecos side. Even the saddles on Santa Barbara Divide are over 12,000 ft elevation, and myriads of alpine flowers, including tiny, aromatic forget-me-nots, bloom here throughout the summer.

Trail continues east along divide, passing over a broad, open Pennsylvanian sandstone ridge, with cliffs facing southward into the Pecos drainage.

28.4   Major trail junction in open saddle just southwest of the broad mass of Barbara Peak. There are two sets of signposts, Santa Fe National Forest and Carson National Forest. Trail to the north drops steeply to the middle fork of the Santa Barbara River, eventually leading to the Santa Barbara campground. Trail down steep saddle to south goes down Pecos River to Pecos Falls.

Sky Line trail continues northeast, climbing great, broad rocky slope of Barbara Peak by means of a couple of switchbacks. South slope of the

ALPINE FORGET-ME-NOT.

peak, toward Pecos valley, is steep, with great cliffs of Pennsylvanian sandstone. Alpine flowers bloom in profusion everywhere along the trail.

29.0   Barbara Peak, south summit (12,626 ft). The highest point on the mountain, about 0.2 mile north, reaches an elevation slightly over 12,640 ft. There are broad benches of almost flat Pennsylvanian conglomerate and sandstone and much rock rubble. Spectacular views lie in all directions, particularly of Truchas Peaks to the west, Taos Range in the far distance to the north, and even the High Plains to the east.

On top of the peak, trails are not clear, but several rock monuments

BROAD EXPANSE OF BARBARA PEAK.
View eastward from trail junction in saddle.

CHIMAYOSOS AND TRUCHAS PEAKS AND THE SANTA BARBARA DIVIDE.
View west across Middle Fork of Rio Santa Barbara from broad southwest slope of Barbara Peak.

mark the routes. A main trail heads northeast along the divide between Rio Santa Barbara and Rio de la Casa, eventually leading to Angostura campground (near Tres Ritos).

For Sky Line trail, head southeast down a rather narrow rocky ridge, with cliffs of conglomerate and sandstone on both sides. The divide is no longer between the Pecos and Santa Barbara drainages, but between the Pecos drainage and Rio de la Casa, flowing eastward.

30.2   Trail junction. Trail has now dropped off the steepest part of the narrow sandstone ridge. A trail branches northwest, angling downward to the head of the south fork of Rio de la Casa, into open meadows, Rincon Bonito. About 0.1 mile past trail junction, Sky Line trail reaches slight saddle on divide (the first east of Barbara Peak). An open talus slope of shale drops steeply southward into the head of Pecos valley.

Soon the trail climbs over the only minor high point east of Barbara Peak and begins to drop toward the saddle at the head of Rio Valdez, over a series of rock benches that dip west at about 6 degrees. Sandstones are less common here than on Barbara Peak; limestones and shales are more abundant. Some of the limestones are moderately fossiliferous, containing horn corals, brachiopods, gastropods (snails), and other fossils. Great talus slopes of shale extend steeply southward toward Pecos valley.

31.5   Trail junction and signpost in broad, open grassy area cut by stream gullies 0.1 mile south of saddle on divide, at head of Rio Valdez (11,790 ft). Trail around slope to southwest goes down Pecos valley to Pecos Falls. This trail is poor for the first mile because it drops down the steep shale talus slope seen from the divide half a mile to the west. Trail to south goes down

Rio Valdez Valley to Mora Flats. Camping places are good along the upper Valdez Valley, particularly at a spring on the east side of the valley half a mile to south.

The pass northward, at the head of the Valdez, has extensive Pennsylvanian shale exposures; fossil gastropods and cephalopods have been collected here. In addition, many flakes of obsidian and a few obsidian arrow points have been found in this pass, indicating that Indian hunting parties roamed the high country within the past few hundred years.

For Sky Line trail, continue east. Trail stays on the south side of the divide and soon enters conifer forests.

32.0   Trail emerges from forests into vast open meadows covering the great broad divide and stretching over 1.5 miles to the east. Trail goes almost due east across the lush meadows. If you need a campsite, turn south from the trail after crossing the meadows about three-quarters of a mile and drop into the gentle head of the Rio Mora Valley. Good campsites can be found within 0.5 to 0.7 mile southward along the river.

For Sky Line trail, continue east near crest of high meadows. There are continual distant views to the east across the High Plains.

33.2   At the east end of the great meadows, the almost flat ridge drops abruptly over 1,000 ft to the east, and there is a breathtaking view down precipitous cliffs to Santiago and Pacheco Lakes, as well as eastward across the lush-green rugged foothills of the Sangre de Cristo.

At the edge of the cliff, the Pennsylvanian sedimentary rocks form a thin, almost flat, veneer; the great unconformity is exposed in the upper part of the cliff a short distance below. Below that, the near-vertical cliffs are composed of steeply inclined Precambrian quartzite—the same rock sequence that forms Truchas Peaks!

Not far west of the cliff top, Sky Line trail swings southward, entering dense forests of conifers after 0.3 mile. Trail goes south for 0.5 mile through the forest, then emerges into a narrow, east-west-oriented meadow. Where the trail enters the meadow, there is talus of Mississippian sandstone (a thin unit underlying the Pennsylvanian, p. 16). In the middle of the meadow, cross the great unconformity onto Precambrian quartzite.

34.1   Signpost pointing eastward to Enchanted Lake View. A side trip across the meadow for 0.2 mile east again brings you to the crest of great eastward-facing quartzite cliffs, with spectacular views to the east, across the foothills to the High Plains.

In this meadow Precambrian quartzites are exposed except at the north edge, where they are overlain by Mississippian sandstones.

For Sky Line trail, return to signpost and continue south. After 0.1 mile, trail enters conifer forests and remains in the trees for almost 0.2 mile. Trail emerges southward into vast meadows strewn at first with numerous blocks of quartzite. After about 0.1 mile, you cross the great unconformity on to Mississippian sandstone rubble.

34.5   Major trail junction and signpost (11,790 ft). Gascon trail crosses Sky Line trail here.

4—East (Elk Mountain) Divide, from Gascon Point to Elk Mountain

This section of Sky Line trail includes virtually the entire East Range (also called Elk Mountain or Rincon), from Gascon Point on the north, to Elk Mountain on the south. The north half of the divide, oriented northeast-southwest, swings more nearly north-south in the south half.

This section of Sky Line trail begins where it crosses Gascon trail on the East Divide, about 0.6 mile west of Gascon Point. Gascon trail marks one of two main entrances to the Pecos Wilderness from the east side of the mountains (the other being the Rociada trail, Trip 8). The trail begins near the end of the road at Gascon and provides an interesting route to the Pecos Wilderness from the east. The Gascon trail is one of the routes over which the Spanish-Americans living in the foothills east of the mountains drive cattle each summer, over the crest of the East Range into the lush meadows of Pecos high country. Note that Gascon trail, as it crosses the broad divide northwest of Gascon Point, has 8 or 10 separate parallel paths. From the crossing with Sky Line trail, Gascon trail descends westward into the upper reaches of Mora Valley, crossing it upstream from the heads of the great canyons on the Mora to the southwest. Gascon trail provides a direct route to Pecos Falls, after crossing Rio Valdez and Hamilton Mesa.

The great meadows covering the divide west of Gascon Point occupy a broad, rounded prominence named Cebolla Peak (Spanish: onion). From the foothills to the east, Cebolla Peak is the most prominent high area along the north part of the divide (11,879 ft); the east-facing cliffs at Gascon Point, composed of Precambrian quartzite, are a glassy white in appearance (color plate 7, top). However, the crest of Cebolla Peak is composed of almost flat-lying Mississippian and Pennsylvanian sandstones and shales. The contact between white Precambrian quartzite and brownish Mississippian sandstone, so evident at Gascon Point, is crossed about half way between the Point and Sky Line trail junction (geology and trail map).

The entire East Range is a great asymmetrical anticlinal fold with a gentle limb sloping westward into the Pecos valley, and a steep, locally vertical or overturned limb partly preserved in the foothills east of the mountains in some areas to the south, particularly on divide between Beaver and Hollinger canyons (geology and trail map). In many places along the crest of the East Range, the overlying veneer of Mississippian strata has been removed by erosion, exposing the Precambrian rocks.

The East Divide, not as high nor as rugged topographically as the West (Santa Fe) Divide, provides many excellent views both to the west and to the east (color plate 6, bottom), as well as interesting geological features. In addition, the East Divide is more remote and less traveled.

Good camping sites, where water is available, are few near the crest of the East Range. At the north end, proceed west on the Gascon trail, from its junction with Sky Line trail, mile 34.5, to Mora Valley, a distance of about half a mile. Farther south, at mile 40.5, possible camping sites are available by dropping three-quarters of a mile westward into Rio del Oso Valley, along the Rociada trail. Still farther south, at mile 43.3, campsites can be found near the spring at Spring Mountain.

From the trail junction, 0.6 mile northwest of Gascon Point southward to the Rociada trail crossing, is about 6 miles; walking time, 2 hours; riding time, 2 hours. From the Gascon trail junction to the jeep road junction in the saddle just north of Elk Mountain is about 13.5 miles; walking time, 5 hours; riding time, 4½ hours.

34.5   Trail junction where Sky Line trail crosses Gascon trail, 0.6 mile west of Gascon Point. Take Sky Line trail south across broad open meadows stretching more than a mile across the broad, rounded rise of Cebolla Peak. Trail skirts the east slope of the highest point, crossing flat-lying Pennsylvanian sandstones and shales. After about 0.5 mile, trail approaches steep dropoff to the east; there are continual spectacular views to the east and southeast, to Hermit's Peak and the High Plains.

35.8   Trail leaves rubble-strewn surface of brownish-weathering sedimentary rocks (Mississippian and Pennsylvanian sandstones and shales) and crosses the great unconformity onto whitish Precambrian quartzite. Trail continues southward near the east rim, with occasional views to the east through small meadows.

36.1   Trail leaves meadow on rim and heads slightly away from the rim, southwestward into corkbark fir and bristlecone pine. Trail continues south a short distance west of rather sharp quartzite divide near the east rim. After half a mile, trail emerges into a great boulder field of white quartzite. Surface slopes down about 20 degrees to the west, and trail is exceptionally rocky. Some quartzite blocks are up to 5 ft in diameter.

37.1   Trail crosses poorly exposed contact, leaving cliff-forming Precambrian quartzite and is now on more easily weathered Precambrian schist that weathers various shades of buff, brown, and reddish brown. The divide is now slightly broader, with a timbered slope to the east, and trail continues south through forest of stunted conifers.

37.7   Trail emerges from forest into an old open burned area, providing the first view south along the ridge to Elk Mountain. The open area extends across the divide and eventually provides views of Truchas Peaks. After a short distance, the trail reenters conifer forests, but occasionally passes through small open meadows and across talus of schist and gneiss.

38.7   Trail crosses from Precambrian schist to quartzite, ascends a rocky ridge southward, and eventually emerges into a broad, open area of white quartzite rubble. Good views of Truchas Peaks at this point.

39.5   Trail crosses great unconformity, climbing onto Mississippian and Pennsylvanian sandstones and shales, then emerges in high open meadows extending southward almost continually for over a mile.

40.5   Main trail junction (11,300 ft). Here Rociada trail crosses divide in vast open meadows (Trip 8). This is the trail over which Spanish-Americans from the Rociada area, to the east, bring cattle into the high Pecos meadows for the summer. It is also a convenient route to the Pecos Wilderness from the Rociada area. Trail to the west goes down Rito del Oso to Mora Flats, and on to Cowles (Trip 8).

Possible camping sites can be found by dropping westward three-quarters of a mile into Rito del Oso Valley. There, small meadows lie both north and south of the trail and creek.

For Sky Line trail and Elk Mountain Divide, continue south along open ridge. This great meadow affords superb views in all directions—Truchas Peaks to the west, the High Plains and Hermit's Peak to the east and southeast.

40.9   Trail enters conifer forests on crest of ridge and continues southward over a good, easy trail. A small amount of Pennsylvanian sandstone rubble can be seen, but no rock outcrops. Although the trail passes through one sizable meadow after about a mile, it generally remains in the forest.

SUMMER RAINS IN THE UPPER PECOS.
View westward to Pecos Baldy from east Divide.

42.7   Trail sign at south end of double meadow. Sign to west says Valle Medio (Trip 9); trail also leads to Rito de los Esteros trail, providing an excellent route to Mora Flats (Trip 8).

For Sky Line trail, continue south along ridge crest.

43.3   Spring Mountain. This is the name recorded by Elliott Barker for this open, rocky, grassy prominence on the East Range, in his book *Beatty's Cabin*. He vividly describes his first view of the upper Pecos basin from this prominence, as a boy of 10, in 1896.

Spring Mountain is particularly interesting geologically. There are two high points. The northwest and highest (11,800 ft) being composed of Mississippian limestone dipping up to 80 degrees to the northwest. Pennsylvanian sandstones and shales lie on the slopes of the hill on the northwest side. Below the Mississippian limestone is about 25 ft of pre-Mississippian sandstone resting unconformably on dark Precambrian amphibolite. The unconformity is in the saddle of the mountain, just east of a Forest Service signpost. The second, southeastern summit of Spring Mountain is in amphibolite.

The trail to the small spring, for which the mountain is named, goes north-northeast into the trees from the saddle where the signpost is located. The spring lies about 0.3 mile away in a small clearing in the trees downslope east of the north end of Spring Mountain. The trail that passes the spring (now unmaintained) is the old Rociada trail. At first, it descends steeply eastward down the divide between Johns and Daily Canyons. Several possible camping sites are located near the spring.

From Spring Mountain, Sky Line trail continues southward along the crest of the divide, crossing dark-colored Precambrian amphibolite, which locally contains scattered white quartz veins. After 0.2 mile the trail enters the trees, mostly corkbark fir and Engelmann's spruce, but also stunted bristlecone pines in the more exposed areas (all trees on the crest are comparatively stunted).

EAST DIVIDE, LOOKING NORTH FROM TOP OF ELK MOUNTAIN.
Cebolla Peak on middle skyline and Santa Barbara Divide at left.

44.4   Trail enters a meadow about 0.2 mile long, marked by amphibolite rubble and old down timber. Entering the trees southward, the trail leaves the crest of the ridge and angles along the east side, a few tens of feet below the wooded summit.

     Throughout the distance from Spring Mountain southward, the trail is exceptionally wide. At one point, an obscure old sign on a tree can still be made out to read "stock driveway." Earlier in the century, sheep and cattle were brought up the east slope from Gallinas Canyon to the saddle just north of Elk Mountain, then driven north along the crest of the East Range, to the trail junction north of Spring Mountain. From there, some were taken to Valle Medio; others to points farther northwest.

45.0   Trail enters small meadow from northeast. Note sudden appearance on trail of smooth gray blocks of Mississippian limestone, similar to those on the northwest side of Spring Mountain. The great unconformity has been crossed again! At south end of small meadow, note talus of Pennsylvanian sandstone and shale. These rock types will be seen for the remainder of the trip southward to the divide north of Elk Mountain. The trail passes mainly through conifer forests, but at 0.6 mile is one large meadow.

46.8   Trail junction and signpost. Secondary trail descends eastward to Beaver Creek. Continue on wide level trail southward through Engelmann's spruce.

47.1   Southern boundary of Pecos Wilderness area, marked by gate with large concrete posts. Faint jeep road extends south along wide trail.

48.0   Road from Willow Creek crosses saddle north of Elk Mountain, at an elevation of 11,400 ft. This point marks the end of the description of Sky Line trail. The trail continues south to the crest of Elk Mountain (11,661 ft) and beyond. See Trip 10 for a more detailed description of Elk Mountain area and the road to Pecos valley.

Suggested Reading

ALPINE FLOWERS
Clements, E. G., 1955, 3rd ed., Flowers of mountains and plain: Wilson.
Craighead, J. J., and others, 1963, A field guide to Rocky Mountain wildflowers; Peterson Field Guide: Houghton-Mifflin.

FOSSILS
Fenton, C. L., and Fenton, M. A., 1958, The fossil book: Doubleday.
Matthews, W. H., 1962, Fossils, an introduction to prehistoric life: Barnes and Noble.
Rhodes, F. H., and others, 1962, Fossils: Golden.

MINERALS AND ROCKS
Dana, E. S., and Hurlbut, C. S., 1953, 3rd ed., Minerals and how to study them: Wiley.
Hurlbut, C. S., 1970, Minerals and man: Random House.
Northrop, S. A., 1959, Minerals of New Mexico: University of New Mexico Press.
Pough, F. H., 1955, A field guide to rocks and minerals: Houghton-Mifflin.

GENERAL
Christiansen, P. W., and Kottlowski, F. E., 1972, 3rd ed., Mosaic of New Mexico's scenery, rocks, and history: New Mexico Bureau of Mines & Mineral Resources, Scenic Trip 8.
Mather, K. F., 1964, The earth beneath us: Random House.
Pearce, T. M., 1965, New Mexico place names: University of New Mexico Press.
Ungnade, H. E., 1972, 2nd ed., Guide to the New Mexico Mountains: University of New Mexico Press.

REGIONAL GEOLOGY
Jahns, R. H., 1946, Mica deposits of the Petaca district, New Mexico: New Mexico Bureau of Mines & Mineral Resources, Bull. 25.
Miller, J. P., 1958, High mountain streams; effects of geology on channel characteristics and bed material: New Mexico Bureau of Mines & Mineral Resources, Mem. 4.
Miller, J. P., Montgomery, A., and Sutherland, P. K., 1963, Geology of part of the southern Sangre de Cristo Mountains, New Mexico: New Mexico Bureau of Mines & Mineral Resources, Mem. 11.
Montgomery, A., 1953, Precambrian geology of the Picuris Range, north-central New Mexico: New Mexico Bureau of Mines & Mineral Resources, Bull. 30.
Sutherland, P. K., and Harlow, F. H., 1973, Pennsylvanian brachiopods and biostratigraphy in southern Sangre de Cristo Mountains, New Mexico: New Mexico Bureau of Mines & Mineral Resources, Mem. 27.

REGIONAL HISTORY
Barker, E. S., 1953, Beatty's Cabin: University of New Mexico Press (Reprinted, Bishop, 1970).
La Farge, Oliver, 1956, Behind the mountains: Houghton-Mifflin.

TREES
Brockman, C. F., 1968, Trees of North America, a guide to field identification: Golden.

Glossary and Index follow

Glossary

AMPHIBOLE—Mineral group composed of a number of related hydrous magnesium silicate minerals.

AMPHIBOLITE—The banded or foliated metamorphic equivalent of dark-colored igneous rocks (basalt or diabase), in which original pyroxene has changed to the black amphibole mineral, hornblende. Calcic-sodic plagioclase feldspar is typically associated.

ANTICLINE—An archlike fold in which strata dip in opposite directions from a common ridge or axis.

ARKOSE—Sedimentary rock containing numerous grains of quartz and feldspar. Commonly derived from weathering and physical breakdown of earlier granitic rocks.

BASALT—A dark, dense, igneous rock consisting of minute grains of feldspar (calcic plagioclase) and pyroxene (iron-magnesium silicate).

BEDDING—Layering as chiefly found in sedimentary rocks: recognized by differences between layers in grain size, color, or other characteristics inherited from the original layers of sediment.

BRACHIOPOD—Marine animal with soft parts enclosed in a shell consisting of two valves. Although individual valves are symmetrical, they differ from each other in shape. One is dorsal (top) and the other ventral (bottom)—not lateral (left and right) as in the clams. Lived from Cambrian to present day; very common in Paleozoic rocks, including those of Pennsylvanian age, where they are the most common fossil in the upper Pecos area.

BRYOZOA—Branching or encrusting colonies of tiny marine animals attached to the sea floor. Lived from Ordovician to present day; locally common in Pennsylvanian rocks.

CIRQUE—Steep-walled semicircular depression at the head of a high mountain valley; caused by quarrying and scraping out of solid rock by movement of glacial ice.

CLEAVAGE—A property of certain minerals to split along perfectly smooth planes. This parting (when developed) occurs between widely spaced atomic planes.

CONCRETION—A rounded body found in sedimentary rocks; usually caused by chemical deposition around a tiny central nucleus.

CONGLOMERATE—Sedimentary rock containing fragments of various sizes, some pebble size or larger. Quartz is commonly a major constituent.

CORAL—Coelenterate animals similar to sea anemones in form, but with the ability to build calcareous platforms and skeletons, usually consisting of tubular or cup-shaped walls containing radial and transverse elements. Lived from Ordovician to present day. Small, solitary individuals with conical shells are locally common as fossils in Pennsylvanian rocks.

CRINOID—A large division of the echinoderms. Commonly called sea lilies because the globular body (with long, jointed arms) grows on a long, flexible stem, giving the animal the appearance of a flower growing from the sea floor. Because of their fragile nature, only fragments are usually found as fossils. Lived from Ordovician to present day; abundant in Mississippian and Pennsylvanian rocks.

CRYSTAL—Geometric shape of a particular mineral formed under conditions favorable for crystallization. The smooth plane surfaces (faces) bounding a crystal are the outward expression of internal atomic arrangement. In a twin crystal (see STAUROLITE), two or more crystal units are grown together according to a geometric law.

DIABASE—Similar to basalt in composition and dark color, but the mineral grains are large enough to be visible to the naked eye.

DIKE—Narrow vein or layerlike body of intrusive igneous rock that has penetrated (while in the form of molten magma) older rock deep in the crust.

DIP—Angular inclination from horizontal of a tilted rock surface, such as on a bed, dike, or joint. Measured in a vertical plane perpendicular to strike. As a rule, geologists measure dip and strike with a special geological compass (Brunton pocket transit).

EPIDOTE—Group of aluminum silicate minerals rich in iron and calcium.

FAULT—Fracture or fracture zone along which there has been displacement of the two sides relative to one another. A strike-slip fault infers horizontal movement parallel to the trend (strike) of the fault. Normal and reverse faults infer up-down movement along commonly steeply inclined fault surfaces.

FELDSPAR—Group of aluminum silicate minerals containing potassium, sodium, and/or calcium.

FOLD—Archlike or troughlike undulations of rocks (anticlines or synclines), best seen in layered rocks. Usually caused by compressional forces in the earth's crust.

FOLIATION—Any secondary, two-dimensional planar structure (as schistosity) in a metamorphic rock. Commonly caused by parallelism of platy or bladelike minerals.

FOSSIL—Remains or traces of ancient animals or plants preserved in the rocks of the earth's crust.

FUSULINID—Extinct marine protozoans with small, spindle-shaped, calcareous shells resembling wheat grains. Internally, the shell consists of closely coiled layers and tiny, elongated chambers. Fusulinids are found only in Pennsylvanian and Permian rocks.

GARNET—Typically, a reddish-brown metamorphic mineral of iron-magnesium aluminum silicate, commonly occuring as somewhat round crystals in mica schist.

GASTROPOD—A large class of coiled mollusks popularly called snails. Lived from Cambrian to present day; locally common in Pennsylvanian rocks.

GEOLOGY—The science or study of the earth, encompassing its interior as well as exterior; the materials of which it is composed, the processes that change and shape it, and the record of ancient life (fossils) found in its crustal rocks.

GLACIER—An extensive body of ice formed in a region where snowfall exceeds melting. Mountain glaciers move slowly downslope as a result of gravity.

GNEISS—Metamorphic rock characterized by parallel bands of different minerals, usually differentiated by diverse lithology, color, or other visible features.

GRANITE—Light-colored, commonly medium- to coarse-grained igneous rock consisting chiefly of alkalic feldspar (orthoclase and sodic plagioclase), quartz, and a small amount of black mica.

HORNBLENDE—A dark aluminum silicate mineral of the amphibole group, containing some iron and magnesium and having a bladed or prismatic crystal form.

IGNEOUS ROCK—Rocks formed from fiery, molten material (magma) solidifying and crystallizing deep down in the crust (intrusive rocks) or out on the surface (extrusive, volcanic rocks).

INTRUSION—A body of igneous rock that has penetrated (when molten) older rock at depth.

JOINT—Fracture or crack in rocks, along the surfaces of which differential movement has not occurred.

LIMESTONE—Sedimentary rock consisting largely or entirely of calcite (calcium carbonate). Limestone is the consolidated equivalent of limy mud, calcareous sand, or shell fragments. Over 95 percent of the materials composing limestones have an organic origin.

LITHOLOGY—The study or general character of rocks; especially their composition.

MAGMA—Molten, fiery material from which igneous rocks cool, solidify, and crystallize. Quickly cooled rock glass (obsidian), however, is noncrystalline.

METAMORPHIC ROCK—Any rock that has been altered chemically and structurally by extreme heat and pressure, causing new structures and minerals to form.

MICA—Hydrous silicate mineral group, with sheetlike or platy structures, having a remarkably perfect flaky cleavage.

MINERAL—Inorganic crystalline compounds that are the integral building units of rocks. Mineralogy is the science or study of minerals.

MORAINE—An accumulation of rock fragments deposited by moving glacial ice. In mountainous country where valley glaciers have been active, moraines are commonly ridgelike in form.

OBSIDIAN—Type of dark volcanic glass having a chemical composition similar to granite. Used by Indians of the past for projectile points.

ORE—A deposit of minerals from which one or more metals can be profitably extracted on a commercial mining scale.

OROGENY (also OROGENIC)—Pertaining to the mighty disruptive crustal forces which culminate in the long-continued process of mountain building. Also termed a mountain-building revolution.

ORTHOCLASE—A feldspar mineral of potassium aluminum silicate.

PALEONTOLOGY—The science or study of fossils (remains of ancient life in rocks), their environments, and the record of their evolutionary development.

PEGMATITE—A very coarse grained intrusive igneous rock, commonly occurring in narrow layerlike bodies. Generally composed of light-colored granitic rock containing quartz, alkalic feldspar, and white mica.

PELECYPOD—A large class of marine and fresh-water mollusks commonly called clams; having two valves, right and left in position, typically equal in size. Lived from Cambrian to present day; locally common in Pennsylvanian rocks.

PHYLLITE—Metamorphic rock similar to schist, in which the parallel mica flakes are extremely minute.

PIEDMONTITE—A pinkish manganiferous mineral of the epidote group; principally occurring as tiny needles or prismatic crystals in metamorphic rocks.

PLAGIOCLASE—A feldspar mineral ranging from sodic plagioclase (albite) to calcic plagioclase (anorthite).

PYRITE—Pale, brassy iron sulfide mineral occurring as cubic crystals, with striations usually present on the faces. Commonly associated with metallic ore minerals.

PYROXENE—A group of related magnesium silicate minerals, some of which are characteristically found in dark basic rocks.

QUARTZ—A colorless to milky white, glassy, translucent mineral consisting entirely of silicon dioxide (SiO_2).

QUARTZITE (also METAQUARTZITE)—Metamorphic rock derived from sandstone, in which the quartz grains have been recrystallized by heat and pressure into a homogeneous, extremely tough, smooth-surface rock.

SANDSTONE—Sedimentary rock consisting largely or entirely of cemented-together sand grains (mostly quartz) imparting a gritty feel. Not as homogeneous and tough as quartzite.

SCHIST—Metamorphic rock characterized by parallel-oriented, coarsely flaky minerals (chiefly mica). The flaky or slabby layering of such a rock is called schistosity.

SEDIMENTARY ROCK—Rock formed by the accumulation of sediments in water, or transported by water, or less commonly, by wind or ice. The sediment may consist of rock fragments or particles of various sizes, of the remains or products of animals or plants, or of the product of chemical action or of evaporation.

SHALE—Dense, soft, usually slabby sedimentary rock, mainly consisting of minute particles of clay minerals, together with varying percentages of tiny particles of quartz.

STAUROLITE—Brown metamorphic mineral of iron aluminum silicate commonly occurring as twin crystals in mica schist.

STRATIGRAPHY—The study of sedimentary rocks, including interpretation of their relative age and conditions of their deposition.

STRIKE—Direction of a horizontal line laid along a tilted rock surface such as that found on bedding. Strike thus shows the horizontal trend of such a surface.

SYNCLINE—A troughlike fold in layered rocks in which strata dip in opposite directions toward a common axis. (see FOLD).

TALUS—A sloping heap of coarse rock fragments at the foot of a cliff or steep slope; same as SCREE, a term more commonly used in Great Britain.

TOURMALINE—A boron aluminum silicate mineral occurring in long, black, prismatic crystals; commonly vertically striated, having round-triangular cross sections.

UNCONFORMITY—An erosion surface separating older rocks (below) from younger rocks (above). A vast time interval of erosion generally precedes deposition of the younger rocks.

VOLCANIC ROCK—Igneous rock material deposited on the earth's surface by outpourings (extrusions) of lava, or eruptions of molten magma to form layerlike bodies of solidified volcanic rocks.

Index

Type faces:	Times Roman
	Text—10/11
	References—8/9
	Subheads—12 pt.
	Display heads—24 pt. letterspaced
Presswork:	38″ Miehle Single Color Offset
	29″ Harris Single Color Offset
Binding:	Sewn & glued
Paper:	Text on 70# Moistrite matte
	Cover on 10pt. Feedcote C1S
	4-Color section on 70# Moistrite matte
Run:	5,000